YOUR STOOLS ARE SAFE IN OUR HANDS

YOUR STOOLS ARE SAFE IN OUR HANDS

LABORATORY INSPECTION

Edie Watney Judd

Matador
9 Priory Business Park,
Wistow Road, Kibworth Beauchamp,
Leicestershire. LE8 0RX
Tel: 0116 279 2299
Email: books@troubador.co.uk
Web: www.troubador.co.uk/matador
Twitter: @matadorbooks

ISBN 978 1800460 201

British Library Cataloguing in Publication Data.
A catalogue record for this book is available from the British Library.

Printed and bound in the UK by TJ Books Limited, Padstow, Cornwall
Typeset in 11pt Adobe Garamond Pro by Troubador Publishing Ltd, Leicester, UK

Matador is an imprint of Troubador Publishing Ltd

Acknowledgement

This book is aimed to educate people about an emerging antibiotic resistance in the world whilst offering humour and inside into a busy Microbiology laboratory. It is a satirical comedy on a yearly UKAS inspection and laboratory testing where readers will have to decipher fact from fiction.

If any character in the book resembles an actual person, it would be a coincidence.

INTRODUCTION

Bacteria were among the first life forms to appear on earth and are present in most of its habitats; in soil, water, and deep portions of the earth's crust, as well as living in symbiotic and parasitic relationships with plants and animals.

Bacteria are vital in many stages of the nutrient cycle by recycling nutrients, such as fixation of nitrogen from the atmosphere, including the decomposition of dead bodies. Bacteria provide the nutrients needed to sustain life by converting dissolved compounds, such as hydrogen sulphide and methane, to energy.

Microbes are found everywhere; they are extremely adaptable to different conditions and survive wherever they are.

There are approximately thirty-nine trillion bacterial cells, outnumbering the thirty trillion human cells in the human body. The largest number exists in the gut flora, and a large number on the skin. The vast majority of bacteria in the body are rendered harmless by the protective effects of the immune system, though many are beneficial, particularly in the gut flora. However, several species of bacteria are pathogenic and cause infectious diseases.

Identification of bacteria in the laboratory is particularly relevant in medicine, where the correct treatment is determined by the bacterial species causing infection. Consequently, the need to identify human pathogens is imperative for the development of techniques for the identification of bacteria. Identification of bacteria is increasingly carried out using molecular methods. The DNA polymerase chain reaction method is a popular techinique due to specificity and speed compared to culture-based methods. However, even using such improved methods, the total number of bacterial species is not known.

Bacterial diversity is vast. There are about 9,300 known species known so far. When bacteria form a parasitic association with other organisms, they are classed as pathogens, which are the main cause of human death and disease and cause infections. Each species of pathogen has a characteristic spectrum of interactions with human hosts. Some species are opportunistic pathogens and cause disease mainly in people suffering from immunosuppression.

Bacterial infections may be treated with antibiotics to kill bacteria or prevent bacterial growth. There are many types of antibiotics and each class inhibits a process that is different in a pathogen from that found in the host. Certain bacteria have an antibiotic pattern. Mixed pathogens can be treated with the combination of antibiotics.

Antibiotics have transformed human health by saving millions of lives. However, in most parts of the world it is easy to take treatment with antibiotics for granted, and the misuse of antibiotics accelerates the emergence and spread of antibiotic-resistant bacteria.

1

FRIDAY

There was a big 'CLOSED' sign in front of the cake and salad bar in the Pathology department staff tea room, and the shelves, under glass, were empty. It was Friday afternoon. All the tables had been wiped down and their chairs upended on top of them. The only sounds were clattering crockery and a murmur of conversation, punctuated by somebody's shrieks of laughter, from the kitchen behind.

At 4:30, the kitchen staff left. Silence reigned.

At five, biomedical scientists from the Infection Sciences section started drifting in from their laboratories. A few had forgotten to remove their lab coats. The rest wore cool summer clothes. Some were taking a shortcut, in and out again through the double doors that led to the seminar room; others, appreciative of sunshine through the skylight after a long day under fluorescent lights, stopped to get paper cups of coffee from the machine.

Half the rooms in Pathology were windowless. Occasionally someone – usually a biomedical scientist called Candida who was worried about her health – would complain about the conditions of work: depleted vitamin D or, occasionally, claustrophobia. Everybody else was resigned to working, unknown, under-appreciated, without daylight and largely forgotten, on the top floor.

Marelyne Cooper, Senior Biomedical Scientist, who was tall, blonde and well dressed, had purchased a gush of boiling brown liquid from the vending machine, but stayed there, poking at the change drawer in an effort to extract 20p. It wouldn't budge.

'Fucking rip-off,' she said.

'Fockin' cah-pitalism,' said Duncan cheerfully from behind her. He had his coffee already. He was from Belfast, with the accent. Marelyne Cooper gave up on the 20p. They followed the crowd.

'Take your lab coat off!'- Hannah pointed at the sign on the door to the absent minded Candida who was just about to sit down.

'Oops.'- she whispered and walked out.

In the seminar room, rows of chairs faced the front, towards a screen. People were taking seats, fiddling with phones, or leafing idly through the *London Evening Standard*.

Joss, a biomedical scientist who doubled up as a technician for events like these, was setting up a laptop and projector on a table. A slide appeared on the screen.

Nanu Diagnostics Incorporated
Clinical Laboratories Division, Europe
Vice President, British Isles and Ireland
Pathology Services
Infection Sciences
Mike Timmerman
Bcomm (Marketing) Mba

The slide disappeared. Joss stopped the projector and scrolled through the rest of the presentation on his laptop. Duncan and Marelyne took seats near the back.

Marelyne asked, 'Who's the infectious Canadian then?'

'Our new boss, darling. Have respect.'- said Duncan and winked at her.

'Acch'- she shrieked. ' I've overdosed on respect. I could vomit a sample.'

Hannah Hayward, the operational manager, a regimental-looking woman with a boyish haircut, wearing a tight suit, marched smartly in. She commanded attention. An unknown man followed her; he was tall, youngish, wearing a snowy shirt, tie and freshly pressed trousers, and carrying a flat leather document case. All eyes were focused on them as they took seats in the front row. Tiger Jones was chattering to the man, who seemed preoccupied with other things. Conversation grew louder as more people took seats.

At 5:05, Hannah looked ostentatiously at her watch, stood up, surveyed the audience, and began fiddling with the mic stand, which Joss had set up alongside the screen to suit a much taller person.

'Hang on.' He adjusted the stand for Hannah and switched the mic on.

'ONE, TWO, THREE, TESTING,' shouted Hannah as if she were in the army, leaning in. The howling sound was painful. She had succeeded in attracting attention.

Joss winced, readjusted the mic's position, and returned to his laptop. Hannah took advantage of the moment.

'Hi! Hi, good people…'

This was uncharacteristically enthusiastic and mid-Atlantic. Duncan and Marelyne, sitting at the back, suppressed snorts of derision.

'I have great news, as well as, er, not-so-good news, so let's get that out of the way first. I've just found out that UKAS inspectors will be back on Monday.' Groans and muffled swearing could be heard in the crowd.

'I know it's very short notice, but all they'll be doing is checking that our transition from CPA to ISO15189 is going well. Our accreditation is not threatened in any way, so you really don't have cause for concern. No panic! No panic at all.' She coughed nervously, and her speech got faster.

'But we all owe it to our employer to have everything absolutely sparkling and super tidy before you leave this evening – all bins emptied and in the right places, no dangerous trailing cables, no finger marks on screens or other surfaces, unused machines and lights switched off, and all equipment as sterile as you can make it. And over the weekend, a bit of extra attention, like making sure your name badge is on your lab coat and that all re-usable PPE has been sterilised.'

There was rebellious murmuring from the crowd.

'I polish the PCR machine,' Marelyne said to Duncan in a low voice.

Somebody muttered, 'The floors are filthy – we need more cleaners.'

Hannah continued, 'We don't want any health and safety issues – no open sharps boxes! You know what to do. Most importantly, don't forget we're also accredited for continuous personal development. Those of you whose competencies are not up to date – you know who you are – I need everybody's folder by 8:30 *Monday morning*, guys and girls! Second thing – wait for it…' Her audience didn't care what the second thing was. They were still reeling from the idea of a weekend spent updating personal paperwork about courses they'd done and lectures they'd attended. '…the person you've all come to see is here.'

'Ohh… *God*,' murmured Marelyne. The man in a shirt and tie stood up.

'We have a *very, very* important visitor. Mike Timmerman is our new VP of medical outsourcing, Infection Sciences, UK!'

Marelyne half-closed her eyes and began to pant dramatically as if having an orgasm. Duncan smirked.

'Our new boss is a very busy man, so we have just fifteen minutes of his time right now. I'll leave it to him to explain exactly why he's honouring us with a visit. Mike Timmerman! A big welcome from all of us.' She clapped. The audience responded with a smattering of insincere enthusiasm.

Mike, who was grinning like a car salesman, thanked her and took the microphone. Beside him there now appeared an oversized headshot of himself, displaying his super-white fixed grin and a head of glossy, thick, chestnut hair too young for his face.

He hoicked the mic stand higher, then lower again, and tightened it. His prompts were on a thin stack of postcards.

'Hiya! Good evening to all of you. It's a great day to be here in this fantastic city.' He glanced at a card. 'I know that all of you guys have *years of experience* in Bacteriology and Virology and M-mycology and Para...' He glanced at a card again. '... Parasitology and, um, all the other ologies in this fabulous Pathology department, and I am truly humbled to meet you.'

He placed the card at the bottom of his pad. Duncan buried his head in his hands. Glancing down at the new card, Mike went on.

'You save lives.' This was true. The slide picture faded and a stock shot appeared; a multicultural bunch of happy, smiling scientists doing something unidentifiable in a sunny, spotless laboratory. Mike was well into his stride.

'I'm here to tell you that Nanu Diagnostics' mission remains to put our team of valued biomedical scientists at the heart of our offer to our customers. This is why we demand fast turnaround times, because patients demand them! And why we emphasise the skills escalator as part of our lean, patient-focused service. And why we are committed to inspiring each and every one of you, while eliminating any non-value-added steps along the pathway.'

'Like stopping for a piss,' muttered Duncan.

'We'll make sure that you all have superb facilities in which to work efficiently, within the strict regulatory environment of the NHS, because we are all stakeholders in this fantastic system.'

Marelyne Cooper raised her eyebrows. Maybe Mike Timmerman was a 'stakeholder', but she personally didn't have shares in this outfit. The slide now said:

Nanu Diagnostics (formerly Multiple Services Solutions PLC)
INNOVATING TOGETHER FOR ALL HUMANKIND
Executive Team
Service Delivery Manager
Deputy Delivery Manager
Operational Manager
Quality Manager
Training Manager
Medical Director
Director of Human Resources
Commercial Finance Director
Chief Scientific Officer
Chief Financial Officer

Mike loosened his tie. It was time to get folksy. Time to get down to convert any sceptics into true believers. The grin was replaced by a serious expression.

'You know – I was looking at a TedX talk recently about bacteria. I know a lot of them are benign, but I didn't know there were trillions of them in all of us, or just how many are downright killers. I wish I'd seen that TedX talk when I was at school. Now that I have, I understand how you people are innovators, moving your profession forward. We want you high-achieving guys, and gals, because I see a lot of you are gals' – the women were cringing – 'to know you are innovating in partnership with Nanu Diagnostics. You're doing a terrific job for our shareholders which deserves to be rewarded in the next round of contracts. Here's what I mean.' A complex diagram appeared on the PowerPoint screen. He stood to one side and pointed at 'PROVIDERS: Independent Sector'.

'That's you and me. Nanu Diagnostics together. Providing cures for infection. Imparting priceless wisdom and saving the lives of sufferers.'

Our values:
Innovation, collaboration, expertise

Emphasis on quality and governance, capital improvement plan, research and development.

Follow the International Organisation of Standardisation (ISO) UKAS (United Kingdom Accreditation Service) which verifies that laboratories comply with the ISO.

Staff started to feel a little uncomfortable; this had been drummed into them for years. They started shifting in their chairs when another slide came onto the screen.

Be the best employer!

Performance objectives:

1. Aim to achieve the highest standards of financial performance and maintain our exceptional operational performance.
2. Assist modernisation to improve and develop our Nanu Diagnostics service in the line with business strategy.
3. Implement robust plans and controls for improved service in our management.
4. Aim to be the best employer for our staff.
5. Change control processes in everyday practice and maintain throughout the division.
6. Comply with mandatory PPE (personal protective equipment) requirements.

'I do hope you understand how important it is to do our best and pass the inspection in the coming days. Your line manager will be available for your appraisals and your continuous professional development.

'But hey! Don't ever forget that your jobs depend on your performance. We are the NHS provider for infectious diseases.' The audience sniggered. *This is going well*, Mike thought, misreading the amusement.

'It's Nanu Diagnostics, not the NHS, that pays your wages. Of course, we can only run this Infectious Science laboratory with ISO-standard accreditation and a contract financed by the City and Hackney Commissioning Control Group, which answers to the NHS commissioning board, and our ten-year contract is up for renewal very soon.' The audience was entirely silent. 'Now, will it be confirmed? I hear you ask.'

A pause. He cleared his throat.

'The Commissioning Control Group will be making its decision in January, just six months away. We have to tender for our contract all over again at the end of this month. Time is short. We have to turn in super-fast turnaround speeds, top competence scores and a fantastically accurate results history. I know you can do it.'

Hannah stepped forward. 'Has anyone got a question?'

Marelyne's hand shot up and so did Duncan's.

Hannah ignored them and nodded at Tiger Jones Hartley, whose hand was up.

He asked, 'Who else is bidding?'

'Probably Capita, Serco, Halo, CYNLAB, Viapath…' Mike said. 'At a guess. Plus, of course, the outfit that currently runs the rest of the Pathology department.'

'Viapath? The ones who changed their name from Serco?' David, a senior BMS asked. They all looked at each other in surprise. 'Why was it necessary to change their name?'

'Because Serco had a bad reputation and they didn't want to be associated with them,' Clare, BMS whispered to her friend Laura, who was sitting next to her.

'Oh, yes, I heard something like that,' Laura added. 'It was on TV. They have a history of blunders and controversies surrounding many of their contracts, including failures, errors and people regarded as "high-risk clients". They are also known to overcharge.'

'Oh! What about CYNLAB? I have never heard of them,' Colin joined in.

'It's full of sinners, ha ha…' Someone made a joke in the back row, overhearing the conversation.

'Tiger Jones's looking to move then,' a voice murmured behind him.

Hannah's mouth tightened. She had only two more questionnaires to call upon, both of them likely to cause trouble. She did wish Mike would stop giving Infection Sciences ludicrous names.

'Marelyne?'

'I'd like to ask a personal question, Mike. Have you always worked with Nanu Diagnostics' Medical division?'

'Not at all. My last job was with Nanu Diagnostics' Waste Management division in Winnipeg, Manitoba.' Suzanne, sitting alone, giggled and turned it into a cough.

'That may surprise you, but Nanu Diagnostics selects its executives with shareholder interests in mind. My expertise is in marketing, and it's thanks to me and my marketing team that Nanu Diagnostics' subsidiary CLEARIT is now the biggest garbage disposal operator in Manitoba.' He ignored the shocked muttering.

'So, please don't forget that none of you will have a job unless I can sell your services to the CCG, the Clinical Commissioning Group. We at Nanu Diagnostics have highly distinguished scientists in your field who will support our tender. I don't pretend to be one of them. My job is to make sure that all of us are playing for the team! And I'm sure we are, especially Hannah, of course. Nanu Diagnostics' success depends on effective leadership! The gentleman beside you has a question as well?'

Duncan stood up. 'More work's being piled into our limited working hours every single week, and we get it all done because doctors need to be able to prescribe the right cure. But we can't carry on like this. When are we going to get a raise? Not an annual increment – a raise.'

The crowed paid close attention. Mike paused.

'A very good question. I'm glad to hear the confidence implicit in it. You will have your job this time next year because we trust you. It's thanks to you that Nanu Diagnostics' contract will be renewed. The industry pay scale is, as you know, based on experience and competence. There is a yearly review when we give you a score for your achievements. The more projects you do – for example, validation of new tests which could save the company money – the better your score and the higher your wages. On top of that, we provide you with a bonus. So, there *IS* an incentive to work harder.' He smiled at the end of his long-winded explanation.

Duncan was still on his feet. 'I see. Experience is what worries me, Mike. If the same four multinationals are in competition for every contract, there's a strong incentive to reduce costs, and a race to the bottom on pay.' A couple of his fans turned to give him the thumbs up.

'Nanu Diagnostics would never force salaries down. Biomedical scientists are too important. You save lives! Without your round-the-clock results, what would doctors do? You do the tests they can't… the ones they can't be expected to administer…' He was out of his depth. 'As for salaries, we are working within the constraints of a health service which has suffered from the austerity programme you have here in England.'

Hannah seized the microphone. 'I'm looking at the time. Thank you so much, Mike. I know you have to be in Belfast tonight. Here in Infection Sciences we applaud your terrific encouragement!'

Duncan and Marelyne looked grim. Everyone else clapped and started to move towards the door. Hannah had to raise her voice.

'*Please* stay late if you possibly can. We need all the reading rooms to be spotless before Monday and if you can't stay now, then I'll want you in on Sunday afternoon. Mike will be back on Thursday in time for the results! He's going to be fully available. He's promised us a buffet lunch! Mike, I know what a busy man you are. Thank you *so* much for sharing your vision with us this evening and we look forward to working with you in the future.'

The audience had stopped listening. They were all shuffling out.

'And please, don't forget, *no* mobile phones in the lab' – Hannah made a last effort to be heard – 'and *no* radio either.' She gave up because, by this time, no one was listening.

Hannah escorted Mike from her office to the lift. He was wearing a jacket, carrying a mac over his arm and wheeling an overnight case.

'I'll come down to the main doors and point you in the right direction,' Hannah said. She didn't have to; he'd already booked an Uber. But she wanted to be seen with a vice president from Nanu Diagnostics. The little, old passenger lift arrived, and they squeezed in.

'That last inspection report was so *picky*,' Mike was saying. 'Especially the safety angle. Somebody working without gloves, I dunno – and the spillage, you know, the broken ankle. But the results, the identification of microbes and viruses, and the treatments seemed very good.'

'We'll make everything spotless and calm this time. I've got boxes and boxes of HiBiScrub. I'll get everybody in on Sunday.' Hannah pressed the button for the third time. The doors at last closed and the lift began its stately descent.

In the many rooms of Infection Sciences, there was activity. Those who had stayed late were hurling months' worth of detritus into black bags. Soon, the bags were bulging with out-of-date wall charts, sets of instructions and copies of *The Journal of Hospital Infection*. Some of these things were quite important and the staff would later regret their enthusiasm. People unplugged equipment to wipe behind it, beneath it, around it and all over with disinfectant cloths.

The mutual mini-crisis – the impending visit of the inspectors – had brought everyone together. They all had to update their competencies, especially in the areas they were working in, as inspectors could ask questions about their work. The photocopy machine was in constant use. Panic set in the air.

2

MONDAY

Monday morning rush hour in the city of London was deafening. Buses and cabs crawled by, cabbies shouted at darting, weaving cyclists, and police sirens approached and faded. David, Mr Broody – in his forties, smart in his best suit, looking like a businessman wearing a wig, otherwise bold, but vain of his looks – was walking fast. Luiza, Mrs Cuddle – a middle-aged, buxom woman, wearing a tight suit with an embarrassing cleavage and red lipstick, with a satchel slung over her shoulder – tiptoed next to him, trying to keep up with him in her new high-heeled shoes. David was rather overwhelmed with the accommodation arranged by Nanu Diagnostics.

He said, 'Terrific hotel, isn't it?'

'Yes, no doubt about that, David. They're part of a public company; they can afford it. When you inspect an NHS lab, you're in the nearest Travelodge. We go down here; it's a cut-through to the west building.'

They turned right into an alleyway. David said, 'They do know we're coming?'

'The operational manager got the email on Thursday. She was probably too dozy to read it, but she replied on Friday, so yes. She's had enough time to give the troops a kick up the backside, but no time to fix anything major.'

'I thought that was our job – kicks up the backside.'

'No, David. Our job is to charm them into thinking that we absolutely love them, while at the same time pointing out their every flaw.'

They hurried across a packed hospital car park surrounded by tall buildings.

In Infection Sciences, Duncan was walking along an ill-lit, locker-lined corridor carrying two paper cups of coffee. He squeezed against a wall to let a well-filled trolley pass and the boiling coffee machine liquid splashed onto his lab coat.

'SHIT!'

'Not today, darling. Mostly piss and sputum this morning.' The mumsy lab technician Charlie grinned at him from behind the specimens on the trolley. He rolled his eyes and pushed sideways through the door marked 'Laboratory Manager'. Tom Clark was at his desk, sipping his coffee while thoughtfully adjusting the angle of his daughter's graduation picture.

'Are they here yet?' he asked.

'Of course. Nine o'clock sharp. I saw them downstairs. They looked like a couple of benefit fraud investigators. It's a woman this time. Rapacious. And a gormless fellah.'

'Mr Nasty and Mrs Nice.'

'You've seen it all, Tom. They should give you an office with a window. Change your perspective – *Jaysus*, this coffee doesn't improve.'

'I want a quiet life.' Tom picked up the big calendar on his desk and showed it to Duncan. 'You see? I have two years and 203 days to go.'

Duncan sighed. 'Time flies.'

'Hannah has got it in for you, Duncan. She gets a call from Nanu Diagnostics and it's like they've turned a key in her back.

She says "YES". Bloody Dalek. "Yes. We can do it. Pile it on. Our slaves will comply." You know what we're getting now? Chlamydia and Gonorrhea screening in quantity. It's from some hospital in Suffolk. Their own lab's been suspended by UKAS, apparently. It feels like the entire population of Ipswich has got an embarrassing disease.'

'It's almost ten o'clock now, Tom. Where are they?'

'They must be here by now... hmm, I don't know. We just have to wait, I guess. In the lift? It does happen a lot lately.' They smiled sarcastically at each other.

Luiza and David stepped into the empty lift, which was remarkable at this time of the morning. It started going up and then came to a stop suddenly.

'I don't believe this! Is it stuck? It's stuck, isn't it?' asked Luiza.

'Hell, it's *stuck*.' David's face wasn't an oil painting. He was shocked. He was never late, especially on his first visit to a laboratory. Punctuality was his motto.

'Oh my God!' Luiza went pale. 'What shall we do?'

'I'm gonna press the alarm.' He did. There was no reaction. 'What's supposed to happen?'

'I think a bell should ring, or it goes through to security. I don't know.'

They heard distant muttering from upstairs. On a landing above, Claire – a young woman from CSR (Central Specimen Reception) – was pressing the 'call lift' button. John joined her.

'The light doesn't even go on,' she said. 'Typical.' She turned and set off down the stairs. John pressed the button a few times, then followed her. A trickle of other people did the same as they left.

'HELP! HELP!' David shouted. Nobody answered. He felt foolish. Events were beyond his control; he hated that.

'Shit. Shit,' he said. He smacked his case's telescopic handle down, laid the case on the floor and sat on it. Only a month ago, he had done a course in crisis management. This was a crisis. He couldn't manage it.

Luiza kept pressing the alarm. A reassuring Jamaican voice emerged from a circle of dots on the control panel. 'Hello. Are you all right?'

'NO,' said David loudly and angrily to the dots. 'Our lift's stopped.'

'Okay. This is Delroy in maintenance. We'll get you out of there. Don't worry. How many of you are there?'

'Two.'

'Anybody who's disabled or infirm or an infant? Or needs medication?'

'No.'

'Which floor did you start from?'

'Ground floor. We didn't go far. We are stuck between the second and third floor. This lift is a fucking antique. We have an important meeting. We have to be there shortly. Do something, for God's sake!'

'I'll try my best, no worries. It does happen now and again. Are the lights still on?'

'Yes.'

'They may go off, but that's nothing to worry about. It's all part of the safety procedure. Please keep well back from the doors. Do you understand? *Do not* try to escape on your own account.'

'Yeah, got it. What are you going to do?'

'We'll do what usually works. There may be noises below you or above you. If our efforts don't pay off, we'll call the fire brigade. Just keep calm. We can hear you at all times. That's okay?'

'Can you do it in ten minutes? We are very late already. I tried to phone, but there was no signal.'

'I doubt it, man.'

'Fuck.'

'I hear you clearly. You can speak to us at any time.'

Luiza and David, whose relationship had begun so warmly, now

16

found nothing to say to one another. Luiza lowered herself gingerly to the grubby floor. She worried about wanting to pee. She worried about having a panic attack. She looked in vain for an air vent. She took her lipstick out of her bag to ensure she didn't smudge it.

David took his laptop from his bag. He typed his password and stared at the wall. Then he put his headphones in, opened iTunes, and listened to everything in his 'Fearless Motivation' collection. 'Success and Nothing Less' took eight minutes. Then 'Today is the Day', followed by 'Time for War', which made his fists clench. And on and on, as David, Mr Broody, psyched himself up to a 'Dynamic Attack' angle.

When, an hour later, Hannah and Tom Clark, Laboratory Manager wondered what had happened to the inspectors as they hadn't heard anything from them, they decided to meet them at the lift, where they found 'DO NOT CROSS' tape and an A-frame 'DANGER' sign. They heard muffled hammering and loud, unknown male voices from the lift shaft.

'Not again,' Hannah said to Tom.

'It will take ages, Hannah, let's have coffee in the staff room.' She accepted.

Far below, Luiza could hear hammering and voices as well. The light went off, and the lift was illuminated only by the glow from David's laptop.

Inexplicably, she began to crave chocolate. Chocolate éclairs…

The noise from overhead became louder. The light went on.

'Hello?' a voice shouted from somewhere above the door.

'Yes?' David whisked his earbuds out and jumped to his feet.

'Please stand well back. *Stand well back* towards the rear wall. You're just below the third floor. We're going to prise the lift doors open. There will be a gap at the top between you and the ledge, and when we're ready, we'll put a ladder across so that you can climb out.'

They both stood back. David touched 'close down', slipped the laptop into his suitcase and zipped it. He shrugged his mackintosh on. The noise from the equipment was deafening. The door slid jerkily open, revealing – further away than either of them had imagined, and lit up in the glare of site lights from above – a dusty, old, red brick wall. This lift had indeed been installed a very long time ago. Both David and Luiza silently forced themselves not to look down. Above eye level was a landing floor, where large black boots could be seen. When the noise stopped, a fireman in a helmet knelt on the ground above and shouted downwards.

'Okay, the ladder is coming. Guide it to land on the floor at the back of the lift.'

The bottom rungs poked across the gap and slid down from the landing's edge. Luiza tried to squash herself into the corner as David pulled the ladder to the floor. Then he grabbed his suitcase in one hand and began to climb upwards.

A voice called from above, 'Thank you, sir. We're ready for you – the lady first.'

David's eyes bulged. *Win at all costs!*

'It's up to you, sir. But it's best to remove the heavier passenger first.'

He suppressed his urge to swear and clambered down. He dumped his case on the floor. 'After you,' he said nastily.

Luiza's face was red and miserable. She set off in her tight skirt. The second rung was impossible.

'I'm going to have to take my skirt off.'

'Whatever.' He sat down on the case, crossed his arms and stared at the floor. 'I won't *peek*. Huh.'

Luiza removed the skirt and began to climb, holding it.

After a while, Luiza's voice wailed from above. 'I can't get any further. It's my tits. They're squashed. It hurts.'

He looked up the ladder and saw an outsize pair of legs, clad above the knee in tight black Spanx.

'Please keep calm. We'll pull your arms.'

'AGH! My skirt. It's gone down the lift shaft.'

'Never mind. Come on, love. We've got you.'

'AAAAghh!'

Luiza's shoes tumbled to the bottom of the ladder.

Above David the two fat legs dangled, frantically searching for a foothold before settling. He heard, 'Breathe in.'

'It's no use. I'm stuck. Could you get some soap?'

Silence, while they all perceived that, however unattractive Luiza's solution promised to be in the execution, it made sense.

'Joe, go in the bog and look for some soap, would you?'

David lost hope. This was a shambles. He curled into a foetal position in the corner of the lift, cradling his suitcase.

'God help me!' he sighed. 'Get me out of here safely!'

Luiza's wide, stately bottom was moving up otherwise-deserted, lilo-covered stairs.

She paused, panting, on a landing. She hadn't slept well.

'Let's go in the other lift, we are late already,' said Luiza.

'Oh no! You can never trust these out-of-the-century lifts again. Let's get the stairs.'

'How many more stairs? Huhh! I couldn't do this every day!'

David, carrying his nylon backpack over one shoulder, kept staring through the huge, dirty window alongside the top flight of stairs. He saw sunlit office buildings, the newest of them towering far above the hospital, and caught a glimpse of a railway line snaking between them at ground level.

'Great view,' he said.

'We can admire London's evening lights later,' she said. 'It's not far, now, come on.'

As they resumed their climb, David noticed mouse droppings on the windowsill. The stairs were over a hundred years old, the corners of the treads choked with dust, and the outside of the window might not have been cleaned since World War II. The 'view' was blurry.

At last, they arrived on the sixth floor. To their surprise, they were greeted by Hannah and Tom, and welcomed as VIPs on the red carpet, which led to the end of the corridor with a big sign on the door – 'Infection Sciences Laboratory' – decorated with flowers.

'Luiza, Mrs Cuddle. Lu, for short.' Luiza smiled.

'David, Mr Broody,' said David, and shook hands with Hannah and Tom.

'I'm sorry this had to happen on your first day,' said Tom apologetically.

'I hope it won't happen again! We are here for three days!'- David commented. ' It was certainly   not a good start of the day!'

'Does it break down a lot?'- Luiza enquired.

'No! It's normally fine,' Hannah lied. It was just too difficult to explain.

Luiza had her stylus and latest-model iPad at the ready, and was about to make a note.

'But there is a separate system for the specimens, of course?' – David's face has shown some concerns.

'Oh, yes. Specimens come by pneumatic tube, or up in the goods lift. They never stop coming.' Hannah made a big deal of opening Pathology's double doors with a magnetic card dangling from a short lanyard around her neck. Luiza made a note of the empty Alcogel dispenser outside the door.

'Security is a priority with Nanu Diagnostics,' Hannah murmured as she struggled with her card. She had to bend forward and swipe the card several times before it worked. The inspectors stood in silence.

Hannah's badge said 'Hannah Hayward: Operational Manager'. She held the doors open. Her smile looked strained and anxiety made her head spin. Mike had left on Friday in furious silence. He'd blame her if they didn't keep their accreditation. Nanu Diagnostics had to pay tens of thousands every time these people visited and if Infection Sciences proved inadequate, she'd probably lose her job. A favourable inspection report was the only possible outcome.

As they were passing through the corridor towards Hannah's office, a notice caught David's attention on the wall. A smiley face advertising top tips to be healthy and happy at work, which said:

NO PRESSURE.
Relax your breathing, take a few deep breaths,
this will help you feel calmer.
Put up pictures on your desk to brighten up your work area.
Celebrate success rather than focusing on what you haven't been
able to achieve.
Take regular, short breaks away from your desk and use them to
be active. Use the time and walk and stretch…

David had taken a mental note of the poster. *Good psychology*, he thought, *for achieving productivity.*

'Would you like some coffee or anything before I show you around?' asked Hannah to get a response, as they were walking down to her office.

'Glass of water, please,' David said. 'It's so hot today.'

'I'll get that for you. You can leave your jacket in here if you like—'

She opened the door to her office. Inside there was a young man.

'Er…this is my office,' Hannah said.

' And let me introduce you to Miklos Gabor, he is Hungarian, and he is the quality manager.'

'Good morning.' He stood up, smiling his thin smile as he extended his hand.

Hannah suddenly moved to the door; she looked flustered.

'Oh!' Her hand flew to her mouth. 'So sorry – I've just remembered something. Give me five minutes, would you? Please do take a seat and I'll just pop out, and I'll get you some water, David – are you sure you don't want anything, Luiza? Tea, coffee—'

'No. We really need to start soon. We are later than expected. We have a lot to get through.'

'I'll just pop into… you know… er… the "powder room" first.' She went to rearrange her clothes and her hair, and put fresh red lipstick on, which complemented her thin, red-framed glasses, which she had just bought in Bond Street. 'I'll be right back.' Hannah left in a hurry.

They waited in silence for a while, when David's patience started to run out. He was on-edge.

'Five minutes? It's more like fifty minutes! What is she doing?'

Luiza looked impatiently at her watch. Hannah's desk was completely bare except for a PC. Filing cabinets lined one wall. On another, cork boards were smothered in layers of NHS data, safety warnings and worksheets, many long out of date. Behind the desk was one tiny mansard window with a view of the sky. Lighting was provided by a fluorescent strip in the ceiling.

Punishment cell décor, thought Luiza, peering across the desk into a corner. She saw a cardboard box, a metre square, piled haphazardly with bulging folders with people's names on. She took a photograph with her iPad. Hannah's idea of well-organised administration was different from her own.

Hannah almost ran along the corridor to the first laboratory – reading room one. She scuttled in and hissed at Duncan, 'Do something for me, will you? Go into Room 2 and Room 3 and get them to clean the windows.'

'We did them yesterday afternoon.'

'I know *you* did, but they didn't. There might be smears – spatters – go right now. Oh, and make sure nobody's got a radio on.'

Hannah waddled at lighting speed to her office from the water cooler with a full paper cup. She nearly tripped over as she approached the double doors.

Inside, Luiza was now sitting down, scrolling through emails and David was rapidly tumbling out a message on his phone, when Hannah burst breathlessly in with a paper cup of water.

'Sorry. I had to make a call.'

'Really?' Luiza said. 'Well, let's get on, then. Drink up, David.'

He gulped water, one eye on the clock, which was now showing half past ten. Hannah opened a drawer.

'Here are your copies of the standard operating procedures for your attention.'

Luiza looked at hers. The last revision, automatically noted at the bottom of the front page, was four days ago. Luiza handed her copy back.

'Would you mind sending this by email as a PDF?'

'Oh, yes. I'll send it as soon as I've shown you the layout.'

'First, let me give you your fire drill diagrams.' Hannah handed them a couple of flyers and went into traffic-control mode, pointing with her arms outstretched. 'The toilets are down that way and the canteen is one floor down. Railway side is north. Stairs and lifts are that way. Most of the labs are on the south side, because those rooms are the ones with big windows.'

She led them out of the room. 'Sorry about this, but I have a conference call and I actually need to attend to it, but first, let me show you the layout and structure of our laboratory. Please follow me to the seminar room. Joss, the BMS, will give you an introduction.'

'Fine,' said Luiza, swerving between two laden shopping trolleys pushed by lab assistants.

'After that, I will take you to CSR, the Central Specimen Reception,' Hannah continued, 'then to the laboratories, where each section will be introduced by an experienced BMS and senior BMS, who will guide you through the reading rooms and will be happy to assist you.'

'I've only got till eleven fifteen, I'm afraid.'

Joss was readily prepared to show the slides to impress the inspectors.

Our values:
Innovation, collaboration, expertise...

Soft music played in the background.

Luiza took a deep breath as she sat down. She had never had that experience before. *Time-wasting*, she thought. She nearly fell asleep.

'Enjoy the show.' Hannah smiled nervously as she closed the door behind her. 'I will be back soon.' She waved.

Joss, feeling like he was on stage, started his talk about the importance of the work in the laboratory. He was confident, having learnt it by heart over the weekend.

'We are one of the busiest and largest hospitals in the country. We are proud to work here. The Infection and Immunology Delivery Unit consists of Microbiology, Virology and Immunology. The Microbiology department has six sections, divided into reading areas, setting up areas and containment level three. The work in these sections is divided into automated and manual work. Personal development and continuous professional development (CPD) is a requirement for HPC registration. Staff attend mandatory training courses, attend at regular case studies and it is the responsibility of each individual to maintain their CPD. It is important to update the competencies in a personal folder, which is checked regularly. The individual has to follow the SOPs (standard operating procedures). The laboratory is CPD accredited.'

He took a deep breath as he was getting exhausted. He had to impress the inspectors. 'Us, biomedical scientists (BMSs), we work alongside the doctors, providing a high-quality service, which is important for the early diagnosis, so the early treatment of patients,' he continued.

'It requires the knowledge of the BMS, who uses the right culture media to grow microorganisms, which are either pathogenic bacteria or commensals. They do the identification of these organisms, which can then be set up for sensitivity testing, so the doctors can report on our findings and treat the patient as soon as possible, especially on the blood culture bench, for sepsis, endocarditis and other areas, to rule out infection on the wound section, respiratory section, meningitis cases, urinary infections, etc.

'The specimen's arrival time to the laboratory is very important in the early diagnosis, as is Infection Control, where a team of nurses and doctors have to identify the route of the infection and take actions. Cleaning, hygiene, and hand washing take a very important role, too. Isolates like MRSA or any resistant organisms or category three organisms are sent to the Reference laboratory for gene typing, so the origin of the pathogenic bacteria can be traced, matched and identified. Early diagnosis means early treatment and quick recovery.

'We, BMSs, save lives. We are the "right hand" to the doctors. Everything has to be controlled in the laboratory by UKAS standards, so we have to ensure that the equipment, media, control organisms, and reagents are working properly and are recorded. Internal and external quality assurance checks are done regularly to maintain our standards. We are proud of our job.

'Doctors regularly give lectures, we get to know about interesting case studies, and improve our services with new information gained from seminars, so we can keep up our continuous personal development. We have an emphasis on quality, i.e. IQA (internal quality assurance), which is done regularly; quality and governance, i.e. EQA (external quality assurance) and CIPs (capital improvement plans); research; and development. Following the International Organisation of Standardisation (ISO) UKAS (United Kingdom Accreditation Service) verifies the laboratory's compliance against ISO.

'Huh.' He swallowed some water from his paper cup.

'Well done, Joss,' said Luiza, yawning. Within five minutes, Hannah reappeared. She handed them lab coats from hooks on the back of the door.

They moved to a big, internal room with windows onto the dark corridor. The double door was labelled 'CENTRAL SPECIMEN RECEPTION'. The inspectors were now primed for action, Luiza with her stylus and iPad, David with his clipboard and biro.

Computers and analysers sat on all the laboratory benches, Pathology services technicians – known as lab technicians or PSTs – were pushing trolleys all around, taking specimens to laboratories, to Virology, Biochemistry, Haematology, and Microbiology. Hannah and the inspectors dodged back and forth in their path. Everything looked clean enough, but the room was, ergonomically, a shambles. David decided that there simply wasn't room for everything.

'What is your name, girl?' Luiza asked a passing PST as her trolley nearly knocked her over.

'Anonymous,' said the girl with long hair in a ponytail, smiling politely. 'Sorry, mam, we are so busy here; not much space, you know.'

Hannah had given this tour before and in her clicking heels bustled quickly ahead, reminding David of a tour guide without a flag.

'As you can see, couriers bring specimens to the desk, or porters bring full boxes up from the wards and the post room.'

On the customer side of the reception desk, a medical courier from 'City Sprint' in motorbike gear was signing a form. On the desk stood containers full of insulated boxes, cool bags and thermal envelopes. The technicians held barcode readers connected to PCs and were taking specimens out of containers, sticking labels on, and organising them into boxes labelled 'BLOOD CULTURES', 'FAECES', 'URINE', 'SPUTUM', 'HVS', and 'SWABS'.

There was a shredder under the desk and a photocopier in a corner. Warning notices were stuck to all of the equipment. The contents of some very old wooden drawers were scrawled thickly in black: 'BIOHAZARD STICKERS'; 'PRINTER PAPER'.

'The specimens come in, get booked into the PC to different sections of Pathology laboratories with EPR (electronic patient records), then labelled and loaded onto trolleys for each department, where the scientists do the tests.'

Hannah saw that David was watching a woman at the desk re-labelling a sample as he made his final note.

'Do you find the trolley system works for you?'- David enquired.

'Perfectly. We have tea trolleys as well – easier to manoeuvre; take less space.' She winked.

'Mmm. I've seen them in other Nanu Diagnostics labs,' David said.

'OK, can we move on now, please, to the laboratories? We'll be back here later today.' Hannah led them into the corridor, where a biomedical scientist was opening his locker. They squeezed past.

'I know it seems overcrowded but—'

'It *is* overcrowded,' Luiza agreed, 'and this was pointed out in the last inspection. It seems that nothing has been done to address that. Is your boss not concerned?'

Hannah looked embarrassed. They stood in a silent group while the scientist took a spectacle case from his locker, locked it and walked past them, saying nothing. 'This is all hush-hush, in confidence, but our vice president told me last week that within the company there is talk – nothing's settled – about moving us to better accommodation. After consultation with the trust, of course. But I don't want that to get out. It would affect staff morale. We're understaffed as it is.'

'Yes.'

'It's just that Nanu Diagnostics could combine all the Infection Sciences rooms with their labs at Bart's and Homerton and move them further out; leave the doctors here and convert the reading rooms for geriatrics. Geriatrics are all over the place; you can't walk about downstairs without falling over a Zimmer frame—'

'Who'd pay for all of this?'

'Well, the hospital would get extra beds, so maybe they'd be glad to see us go.'

'Maybe, but the trust would have to convert the rooms and install bed lifts. Where do Nanu Diagnostics want to move you to?'

'A warehouse near the Olympic Park in Stratford.'

'No intention to install TLA there?' asked Luiza.

Hannah looked blank. 'TLA?'

'Total laboratory automation,' David chipped in.

'Oh, you mean that all-in-one sys… Oh, no. No. Not as far as I know.' Hannah didn't seem to have thought of this before.

'And you rotate your microbiologists between rooms regularly?'

'Yes. Of course, they'd have to work between here and Stratford for a while.'

A lab technician emerged from the CSR pushing a trolley. They fell silent. When he'd gone Hannah confided, 'A move wouldn't be popular.'

'Change rarely is.'

Luiza said, 'Surely moving to Stratford means you'd have to run a complex twenty-four seven shuttle service for specimens. There's potential for human error.'

David agreed. 'A courier left TB sputum in a high street department store once. And if you stick biohazard substances in an icebox on a motorbike and that bike crashes, well…'

'At the moment, my bosses are considering costs. We're looking at a CSR hub here, and then the tube, except for night-time, when we could courier—'

'The *tube*?'- David raised his eyebrows.

'The *central line?* Infectious specimens transported by tube?'

'Well, Mike thought… I mean… we could use the seven-minute, high-speed train from St Pancras. Or the Jubilee – no, no, we couldn't use that – it's not set in stone yet,' Hannah ended weakly. 'As I said, that's confidential.'

Luiza's nose momentarily wrinkled in disgust as they continued along the long corridor, passing the washing up area, towards the Microbiology laboratory.

'There's a noticeable odour in here,' Luiza said.

'That's waste being autoclaved.'- said Hannah.

'I guessed. Oh!'

'There are *three trays* of urine going into the autoclave today,' Hannah explained.

'That's rather a lot.'

'We do have non-stop work at the moment.'

'And a backlog?'

'Yes… because the autoclave breaks down now and again… but we are trying to clear the backlog as soon as possible,' she added quickly. 'In fact, we just received a new, modern, up-to-date autoclave, which is being tested as we speak.' She was about to say something else when a screeching voice came from Andy, a leading MLA, (medical laboratory assistant), who was leaning into the autoclave with half of his body, searching for the probe in the back.

'Jesus Christ! You want to cut my head off?' He jumped out fast, his reactions as quick as lightning. He was so angry with the passing MLA who had pressed the button by mistake as he was rushing to put more tins in the other autoclave. Andy was only concerned about his safety; he didn't care about the inspection.

The inspectors and Hannah looked at each other in shock and they walked in to see what had happened.

'Are you OK, Andy?' Hannah asked in a caring voice.

'Yes, I'm fine. Huh! It scared the life out of me! It was an accident, of course. It could have been worse.'

'Isn't there a safety button?' Luiza asked in a concerned tone as they walked out of the room.

'Yes, of course. The new machine is just being tested. It will never happen again, I can assure you.'

'Alright, David and I will come and see how it works tomorrow morning, first thing. We must know and make sure that it works fine with safety standards.'

'Sure,' Hannah sighed. 'Now, if you don't mind, I would like to take you around the lab and show you the way specimens pass through the system.'

Hannah escorted the inspectors in. The biomedical scientists and MLAs wore gloves, white lab coats with name badges on, goggles and face shields as they were setting up specimens or preparing stains.

The room was big, light and warm. A wall of windows, blinds halfway down against the sun, faced south across a courtyard to another hospital building. Scientists were concentrating on their work at benches crammed with microscopes, computers, stacks of culture dishes and diagnostic equipment. There was a gentle hum from the machines. As in the CSR, pinned or stuck on every cork board and piece of equipment were notices in capital letters with brightly coloured hazard symbols warning about danger: notices on 'patient alert' on each bench, hand washing, turning machines off, not running machines beyond a certain time, doing this or that only when wearing PPE, and so on. These admonitions had been comprehensively weeded on Friday, but there were still so many that they blended into the background.

Hannah started her introduction. 'The Microbiology department has six sections divided into reading areas, setting up areas and containment level three. The work in these sections is divided into automated and manual work. This is the setting up area. Faeces, sputum, urine, swabs and tissue samples are organised by bench. Now, let me introduce you to Tiger Jones.'

She wanted to carry on when suddenly something heavy hit the floor. 'That's another box of specimens coming in now from BUPA. That is extra; we have a contract with them.

'I see... when do you have time for that, may I ask?- said Luiza.

'There are dedicated people who stay behind and do overtime for that. This is Tiger Jones. He's the senior biomedical scientist in charge of this section – Tiger, this is Luiza, Mrs Cuddle, and David, Mr Broody, from UKAS.'

Tiger Jones – a tall, slim young man with curly black hair, Mediterranean-looking, with warm, brown eyes and broad shoulders – who was slumped on a tall, uncomfortable stool, frowning at a computer screen, turned briefly.

'Hello, Luiza, hello, David. I'll be your point of contact here when you come back.'

David thanked him. Luiza was silent. Tiger Jones really was unusually handsome. He said to Hannah, 'Just to let you know, we could only make five copies, and the printer guy can't come till Friday.'

'OK.' They moved on.

Luiza pulled herself together. 'Average turnaround time for a specimen, pre-analysis?' she asked Hannah.

'Er… I'll come back to you on that. It will vary by time of day and what kind of specimen it is, of course. We have to comply with turnaround times, otherwise we get fined,' she said quickly.

'Hmmm. That's not so good.' Luiza raised her eyebrows. 'The layout is tight, isn't it?'

'Well, we're too busy to change it.'

David, who had quickly counted heads, asked, 'Do you often have so many people working here?'

'Always, except at night. Late afternoons are the busiest.'

'I can only see five PCs.'

'Yes. We have asked for three more.'

Luiza said, 'It's hard to see where you'd put them.'

'Yes.'

A bleep went off. Duncan passed them in urgency.

'Excuse me,' he said, hurrying to the 'specialist section'.- Duncan made a quick move towards the laboratory door labelled Room 3.

'That's for urgent specimens,' Hannah explained. 'We had meningitis cases twice last week, once viral and once bacterial.'

'What about overnight?'- asked Luiza.

'There is one BMS here all night, and one Infection Sciences microbiologist doctor on call, who covers both Microbiology and Virology. The Virology BMSs don't work nights.'

'Why's that?'

'Company policy, and it is not in their contract. Virology, Microbiology and Immunology together make up the Infection and Immunology Delivery Unit, so if somebody needs an urgent test done like HIV or Rapid Flu, and now the dreaded COVID-19 PCR test. The duty BMS in Microbiology will have to do it.'

'More and more work is piled onto us.' – a grunting noise came from Colin, who was getting fed up with the pressures and stress at work.

'We do have a lot of rapid flu tests done at night, especially in the winter,' Hannah said, disregarding Colin's comment, 'but it brings a lot of money to the company, and at the same time this test is very important because patients are not admitted to wards if they are tested positive, which, of course, saves beds.'

'So, what's the turnaround time pre-analysis to post-analysis for *urgent* specimens?'- asked Luiza.

'Oh… under two hours depending on the test of course.'

'Can you be more specific?'

'No.'

'Specimen arrival time is important in early diagnosis, for example, of meningitis.' – Hannah quickly added.

'OK. We have the general idea,' Luiza said. 'Let's move on. We can make our observations in detail tomorrow.'

'Yes of course' – Hannah gave a beaming smile. She wished the inspectors had disappeared into thin air.

'So, this is the "specialist" section we have briefly talked about, where sterile fluids like CSF and tissues are set up.'- she added quietly.

Duncan, at his bench facing the window, had been adjusting a gram slide under a microscope. He turned as they came in and walked over to them.

'Duncan is our senior in this room. He looks after the blood culture section too. Duncan, this is Luiza, Mrs Cuddle, and David, Mr Broody, from UKAS.' They were introduced. 'Duncan will explain everything tomorrow.'- Hannah said.

He had a large grin, showing his perfect, white teeth. 'I'll be here all the time, so if you want any information, you are welcome to ask.'

David thanked him. Hannah, moving them along, said, 'It's routine Bacteriology, although we are doing new projects, advanced techniques as well and validating them to improve our service. Audits are done regularly, too.'

'I see. Do you have time for them? Do you work with clinical scientists?'

'Oh yes. It gives us a better appraisal score and it counts towards our CPD, which is expected from each member of staff.' – David explained.

'Now, I suggest we move on.' – Hannah said quickly. She scuttled breathlessly ahead, hurrying them down the corridor. 'Since we're passing, this is the doctors' room.'

All three peered in through thick, wired glass, like a bullet-proof window.

'They're busy all the time, receiving our reports and assessing results. Nothing leaves the lab without their consent. And they give us talks on interesting case studies we can learn from. Again, it's good for our CPD.'

Of the doctors nearest the window, facing the inspectors on either side, one was focused intently on his screen while munching on a Kit-Kat, and the other, whose name badge said 'Dr Death', was making notes onto a pad as she prepared for the 'case study' of the week. In the corner, with his back to the inspectors, a doctor was scrolling through a website bearing the logo MEDI-STAFF

NZ. He stopped at a picture of a glamorous surgeon, capped and gowned, above an article headed:

MEDICAL DOCTORS' SALARIES, NEW ZEALAND

Some sixth sense made him turn. Hannah's big, anxious face was scanning the room through the glass. The door opened, and she brought the inspectors in.

All the PCs in here were connected to the hospital's internal system and showed the biomedical scientists' identification of pathogens within each specimen, along with the appropriate antibiogram. White coats hung across the backs of chairs. One doctor, without taking her eyes off her screen, was muttering to the one next to her.

'They've tried everything else. The patient has severe cellulitis in his left foot, apparently. A deer bit him, it says.'

'Hi, everybody,' Hannah said loudly. 'Just showing the UKAS inspectors around.'

Luiza and David took in the scene. There was a stained coffee table scattered with dog-eared copies of *The Lancet* and the *BMJ*, and some specialist medical magazines still sealed in transparent polythene. On the walls behind the benches were long rows of shelves crammed with files and a small selection of books, like *Academic Press Dictionary of Science and Technology*, *Manual of Methods for General Bacteriology*, and also the standard works on Histopathology, Biochemistry, Mycology and Parasitology. A poster announced:

NO POLITICS.
NO SWEARING.

Somebody had scrawled 'PRECIOUS LITTLE SEX EITHER' below.

Under that, in different handwriting, they read:

NO TIME
NO MONEY

Luiza noticed that one young junior doctor was Googling '*Giardia lamblia*'.

'Just a quick intro to the UKAS inspectors, guys,' said Hannah. 'They're Luiza, Mrs Cuddle, and David, Mr Broody – you'll see them around until Thursday. They'll drop by.'

A doctor tried to suppress his laugh.

They waved, said 'Hi', or nodded amicably and carried on with their discussion.

'It does say "condition worsening".'

'I'd pass it. Even if it is banned, what else can they try?'

'I'm not sure. I'm going to call Freddie.'

'Good idea. If in doubt, call a consultant.'

'Are you presenting a case study this week?' David interrupted their conversation.. 'We would like to come.'

'Yes, I shall present a case on Wednesday.'

The voice came from the back of the room, from a young doctor. 'A patient has just been admitted with osteomyelitis, with maggots, cobwebs and spiderwebs in his wound. He has been flown back from the Far East. This was an ancient remedy used by the Romans and Greeks. Accident and Emergency asked our opinion about this case, and we advised them to keep the maggots and spiderwebs in until we find the right antibiotic.

'Cobwebs have antifungal and antiseptic properties, minimising the infection and efficiently stopping bleeding as they are high in vitamin K, which triggers blood clotting. Maggots consume and clear away both bacteria and deep wounds, and promote healing by secreting allantoin.'

'Oh! Very interesting. We shall look forward to the case study.

'Hmm.' – David gave a loud sigh as he was stroking his chin. He was about to leave the room when he quickly turned back

35

and asked, 'Tell me, does every new doctor in the hospital receive training in the first few weeks?'

'Oh, yes. We are very impressed with the training by the experienced staff and the consultant of the laboratory. He takes every case very seriously.'

'Good.' - David was satisfied with the answer. 'See you on Wednesday, then.' He smiled politely deep in thought. On their way out they got stopped by an enthusiastic voice coming from the back of the room.

'By the way, Dr Greenwood is giving a talk on ESBL and other resistant organisms. I thought you might like to know' - said a junior doctor. It would be worth to go to.

'Oh, thank you for letting us to know.'

'What do you think, Luiza?'

'I think we might learn something.'

'Oh, yes, of course.' She agreed.

Hannah and the inspectors turned out to the corridor, leaving the doctors worried about the deer bite continuing their conversation.

'Walking quickly ahead of the inspectors, Hannah rounded a corner and was smacked in the face by a heavy locker door swinging open on its hinges.

'Oh, are you all right?' David asked.

'Just about. Maintenance was supposed to fix that.'

'Nanu Diagnostics uses the hospital's maintenance staff?' Luiza whisked out her iPad to note the answer.

'Sometimes. Er... anyway... let me show you reading room two.' There was a sign on the door with large letters:

YOUR STOOLS ARE SAFE IN OUR HANDS

'The usual senior's on maternity leave, but Lucy Bullock is our stand-in.' Hannah pushed the door open. It looked like the first room, sunny and quiet. There were incubators and stacks of lidded culture dishes. Cables dangled from plug sockets, inconveniently located above the window, and trailed along the benches to machines. Plastic boxes with forms labelled 'FAECES' were stacked under a bench. A young biomedical scientist called Laura with a pipette was filling parts of an API strip with a bacterial solution.

Another was spreading a culture onto an agar plate. People were working silently, mostly reading culture plates for urine, respiratory samples and stool cultures. Having introduced Lucy Bullock, Hannah whished the inspectors out of the room. They'd be back in the afternoon.

'Are those used autoclave bags? …in the boxes on the floor?'- Luiza asked.

'Well, we are rather pushed for space.'- Hannah answered quickly as she was looking at the floor. She felt embarrassed, she didn't know what to say.

Anvi, a short, plump BMS with curly hair, turned to the inspectors and took over the conversation, explaining, 'Used specimens that need autoclaving before disposal are normally bagged up and stored in a fridge for a week. But the fridges are full because there are only two autoclaves, so we have to keep the full bags in containers until there's room.'

'I see. Thanks, Anvi Patel.' – Luiza said as she was looking at her name badge. 'That is an unusual name, isn't it?'- she asked.

'Yes, it is. It is an ancient Indian name.' She smiled back at her. She liked talking about herself. 'Anvi means that everyone has to follow what I say. Sometimes they do, ha ha.'

'Hmmm. We are back tomorrow to see the workflow in detail.' Luiza sounded serious.

'Okay, shall we move on?' Hannah held the door open. This was awful. They'd spotted the boxes, they'd recognised the backlog, and Luiza, at least, wore a permanent, superior sneer. Surely only disapproval of the whole lab could have inspired her to look so scornful. Hannah hurried them down the corridor. *Oh God*, she thought, *Luiza is about to ask another bloody question.*

'Can I just ask you a little more about the autoclave problem? Do you feel you're taking on more work than the unit can cope with?'

'No, no. I mean, Nanu Diagnostics managers and staff like to work flat out, because it's so fulfilling. I mean, we're saving lives! Our reporting is very good; the doctors don't often come back to us. Sorry to move you on so fast, but I need to show you containment level three and after that, Duncan can take you to Virology. They're expecting you.'

She hurried ahead. 'Oh.' Her phone alerted her to a message and she looked at it as she opened the door to reading room three. 'Umm... sorry, I have to leave you shortly; my conference call's been brought forward fifteen minutes.'

Containment level three was entirely internal to the building and stood like a cube against a corridor wall. Its doors and corridor-facing windows were pasted with fierce warnings in heavy capitals about access being restricted to certain lab staff *only*. Hannah and the inspectors stood outside. Thick glass separated them from the gowned, gloved and goggled scientists within.

'This is containment level three, and the lobby, as you can see, has interlocking doors with a monitoring system. The code changes weekly and this week it's 1928, the date of discovery of penicillin. They're expecting you. PPE, a green gown, is ready for you in this cupboard here – just take it and dispose of it as instructed when you leave. You see the man in the turban? That's Paramjit, he's the senior.'

'OK. That's fine.'- Luiza acknowledged it with a nod.

Hannah was in such an obvious state of anxiety by this point that neither Luiza nor David wanted to interrupt with questions. She indicated the scientists at work inside. They were working with specimens which might contain category three pathogens, like mycobacterium tuberculosis. She rang the internal buzzer for the attention of the scientists at work inside. She left them and headed back to her office with minutes to spare.

She had spent the weekend comfort-eating, talking to her cat and feeling terrified of losing her job. Or demotion, which would probably be worse. She'd never met Mike's immediate superior, an executive VP called Peter Barnet based in Dublin; she'd have to talk to him now, she knew. Mike would definitely stab her in the back. Unprepared, and trying to speed-read the agenda in front of her, she connected to the conference call from Mike and his boss.

The inspection was the important item on the agenda. Hannah spoke positively about the possible outcome on Thursday. She told them that the inspectors would report their results to all the Microbiology staff at lunchtime. Mike interposed.

'You better make sure we get a result, Hannah. I've invited a doctor from the commissioning control group to come over on Thursday.'

'For the results?'

'Hannah, I want to get us a renewal. *Everything's* got to work.'

'Fine. It will…'

It was a brief interlude in an otherwise constructive discussion, but Mike's aggression made her feel like a worm.

She struggled through the afternoon in her office, keeping out of everyone's way. She had developed a slight, sporadic tic. She needed a fag desperately, but she had no time; she had to get through some emails from upper management.

Joss, the technical biomedical scientist, was eating beans on toast and reading the *IT magazine*. He was alone at a table for three in the tea room, but the tables were slowly filling up. Tiger Jones came over with fruit juice and his usual box of vegan sandwiches.

'Hi, Joss. I thought you were on nights?'

'Couldn't make it. Signal fault in Sheffield. I waited forty-five minutes for a bus and gave up. Hannah got Carla in instead. She was still here when I came in this morning and she said she'd been working all night.'

'Yeah. They're using us to fulfil outside contracts and we should get a cut of the profits from them, too.'

'We had one hundred faecal samples yesterday afternoon, in a batch from some hospital I've never heard of. And all the resistant screens on top! Hundreds of them!'

'I saw them,' Jim, a well experienced BMS agreed.

'They have got a nerve. When are we supposed to fit it all in? By the time my kids come home, I'm on my way out again. I didn't sign up for night work. I thought it'd be about once a month. It's once a fortnight and the money is rubbish.'

'Anyhow, let's not have a moan-fest,' said Tiger Jones, but Joss carried on.

'I wish we had a union worth a bean.'- Jim said.

'Yeah, I agree.'- Joss was raising his voice, his eyes were bulging out as he could hardly control his anger. 'Hannah doesn't stick up for us. She just wants to keep her job. She's worse than the marketing prat who looks like a crooked car salesman.'

'Calm down Joss.' – Tiger asked him politely. 'It's inspection day'

'Yes, I know. But we ought to complain. Hannah always says the same thing: "It's company policy".'- 'It's because they won't even pay the overnight supplement and there is only one BMS working at night for twelve hours without a break. I want more than twenty quid for that level of responsibility and no sleep.'

'Well, that's Nanu Diagnostics. They've got to pay fat dividends to shareholders. They're more important than we are.'- Jim added to the conversation.

'It's worse than being a junior doctor.'- said Joss. 'Makes you wonder why we bothered with a four-year degree, doesn't it?'

Marelyne appeared with her lunch. 'Mind if I sit here?'

'Hello. Great.' Jim gave her a big smile.

'Nothing could be worse than being a junior doctor,' she said as she sat down.

'At least they get off with the nurses,' Joss said. 'We are just drones in the attic.'

'It's not sexy, dealing with bodily fluids all day,' Marelyne said, 'but at least we don't have to touch people.'

Jim laughed. 'Since when did you want to…?'

She shook salt onto her chips.

'I mean, if I get a swab from something really gross, like a pus-filled sore, it's just another bug under the microscope. If I were a doctor I'd have to take hold of somebody's veiny, old leg, and prod, and eugh.'

'Christ.' Jim put down his sandwich. 'And bon appétit to you, too.'

'I always thought you were one of the people who really liked their job here,' said Joss curiously to Marelyne. 'I didn't know you'd ever wanted to do anything else.'

'I wanted to be a musician.'

'I never knew that,' Jim said.

'You didn't ask. I teach piano part-time. I have five pupils doing their grades. I just juggle the hours. It helps with paying the bills. Half of the people in this lab have a second job, but at least I enjoy mine.'

'Yeah. Delivery last year,' Joss said, 'now I'm an Uber driver.'

At five o'clock, Hannah was thinking of going home early, when the phone on her desk rang. She heard Peter Barnet's voice. Her heart sank. This was it, then. Nanu Diagnostics were going to let her go. She'd have to sign up with an agency. She felt her cheek twitching. The tic was getting worse.

Peter asked how she was. He sounded conversational, not hostile at all. She responded in kind, trying to sound upbeat, but she knew what was coming.

Then she heard him say, 'I spoke to Mike after our conversation this morning.'

'Oh. Really?' Here it came.

'It seems he's been overstressed. You know, culture shock, anger management issues… he's going to apologise for his behaviour towards you.'

Hannah's fears melted away. She was infused with a warm, emotional glow. Peter Barnet, director, Infection Sciences, Great Britain and Ireland, carefully rebuilt her ego.

'I believe he was frustrated by the location your people have to work in. But, of course, that is beyond your remit. You are a perfectly good manager. You know your stuff. I think you can go far with Nanu Diagnostics.'

'I hope so.'

'I'll be in London later this month and we can discuss resources, yes? You have a great career ahead with us. Hannah, I want you to be frank with the inspectors about any problems with the building. Mike's told you there could be an alternative location. I'm not so sure. I think we should present that to the CCG as an opportunity that only we are prepared to offer investment in technology.'

Hannah was emboldened by such confidence. She said, 'That sounds good. But there is something else and it's arisen during the inspection. It is an awkward issue. We're overwhelmed by new work. I am worried that if this goes on, one day we may let the NHS down – you know, our turnaround time may suffer. That's the risk we're running.'

'How's that?'

'We're getting more private work than we expected.'

'Where from?'

'I believe Mike's bringing it in. It's great for our shareholders but it's too much for my team here. We are constantly running a backlog. People call in sick, they can't cope, so they are leaving, and we have to employ locums, which cost more money.'

'I see. Are you saying that we should have a separate set-up for private work? In a different place?'

'Yes.' It hadn't occurred to her.

'Just out of interest, I'll ask – would you like to run it? It would be a promotion.'

Her distress melted away. Elation took over. 'Of course. I would like it very much. Is it a possibility?'

'I'll look into it. Leave it with me, Hannah.'

She put down the phone, ready to take on the world. In fact, she felt perfectly ready to apply for a job not unlike Mike's. She picked up her credit card and headed for Harvey Nichols.

That evening, the inspectors dined at their hotel. They had a three-course meal with the finest wine. A waiter had just removed the empty plates from their first course, which was 'smoked mackerel rillette, brown shrimp and seaweed cracker'.

'I never bothered much with starters in Scunthorpe,' David said, 'but that was *amazing*. And this wine is delicious. Shall we raise our glasses to Nanu Diagnostics?'

'Good idea.' They clinked glasses. Luiza continued, 'Five-star accommodation at this Marriott Hotel! If I didn't know better, I'd say Nanu Diagnostics was offering us an incentive.'

'Perish the thought.'

'No, we're not that cheap.' They giggled. 'But we will come back,' Luiza said. 'That call I got this morning – it was from someone on the CCG. She's quite new, apparently, and she wants to be here for the results on Thursday. I couldn't turn her down.'

'Oh. Really?'- David was surprised.

'Just as an observer. Anyway, that lab is better than it was. The staff seem competent. It's the layout.'

'And the IT. It really should interface with *all* of the hospital system. It definitely needs an upgrade.'- said David. 'All that paper! I do wonder about Hannah. She may well be a biomedical scientist promoted above her ability. I think a manager should raise hell if IT doesn't interface with the hospital system.'

'Tomorrow's going to be fun, hacking through the folders.'- Luiza was rubbing her hands in satisfaction.

'Tomorrow?'

'Yes, and we can spend Wednesday dropping into the reading rooms to question specific individuals about their expertise.'

'I like that part best. I always wanted a job that guaranteed popularity.'

Their main courses arrived, perfectly presented: 'fillet of gilt-head bream, Swiss chard, sea vegetables and anchovy dressing'. They picked up their knives and forks.

Luiza said, 'So, how does it feel to escape from the sticks?'

'Great. I'm going to see my brother on Wednesday night. He lives in Clapham. Is that OK with you?'

'No problem. Just email your results to me and I'll bash it all into a draft report when you're out. It won't take me long and we can discuss it on Thursday morning.'

Luiza was getting ready for bed when there was a knock on her door. A man dressed in female clothes, with high heels and wearing heavy makeup appeared.

'Hi, darling,' he said in a high-pitched voice. 'Are these boobs real? Am I your first guest?'

Luiza was astonished. 'I think you have come to the wrong place,' she said and tried to stay calm. 'There is a party going on next door. I can hear them. Maybe you should join them.'

'Oh, yeah. Sorry.' He gave her a flirty look as he left the room.

That night was a very hot night and the party was going on forever. The music was getting louder as she tried to sleep. She just about dozed off when a mosquito flew into her inner ear and kept buzzing. By this time, she was so tired, she needed to sleep badly. She tried to get the mozzie out but in vain; it was still buzzing. She got up in anger. At first, she didn't know what to do, when suddenly she remembered that there was a water bottle in the fridge. She squirted the water very hard from the bottle and with success. The mosquito came out dead and the buzzing stopped at last.

3

TUESDAY

Luiza overslept; she had a bad night and she would take her revenge on the lab staff.

'Hmm, raining. Grey sky, miserable day,' she said to herself as she looked out of the window and pulled a face. 'Never mind, let's go down and have breakfast.'

'Ready for it, Luiza?' asked David at the breakfast table, after wiping his thin lips with the soft hankie and sighing in satisfaction.

'Ready for what, David?' She laughed. 'Let me have a piece of that scrumptious chocolate cake. Don't worry, we won't be late, just call a taxi. Nanu Diagnostics will arrange the bill.'

She was well-prepared and made sure that she would look her best. She rearranged her hair and put her favourite red lipstick on.

'The taxi is here,' a voice came from the reception. They had both made themselves comfortable in the taxi when, after a few minutes, it suddenly broke down. Panic set in. They looked at each other in despair. They couldn't afford to be late on the second day as well. The hospital was on the other side of the river.

'What do we do now?' asked David.

'It's alright, I am calling another taxi on the radio. Sorry about that,' said the driver.

'Thanks for that, our savior.' But a few minutes later, the next taxi stopped. It had run out of petrol.

'Oh no! It's impossible! I can't believe it! 'We will be late again!' Luiza was working herself up by the minute, panting.

'Come on, Luiza, we have to walk,' said David impatiently. 'It's not far now.'

They both ran, but Luiza's shoes were not made for running.

'Wait, wait, David…' she sighed.

'I would pick you up, Luiza, if you were not so bloody heavy. We are not far, come on!'

Their task for Tuesday is reading SOP documents and working separately in the reading rooms.

When they arrived, the daily 'huddle' had already started. Any issues and changes were raised and the staff listened. It had only lasted for five minutes, when the radio blasted out 'This Will Be The Day' by Casey Lee Williams and Jeff Williams. The staff started their morning exercises. David's jaw dropped to the ground. Luiza's face was as if she had seen a ghost. They had never seen anything like it.

'Company policy,' Hannah said, smiling. 'We think exercise is good for the staff, it makes them happy and they work more efficiently.' She moved away, leaving the inspectors in their bafflement. At that moment, Colin rushed in like a steam engine. He was worried he would get put in the 'late arrival book'.

'Sorry,' he said apologetically. 'My train was late and the lift didn't come.' He wiped the sweat from his forehead and slumped his heavy body onto a chair. He had no energy for exercise. Embarrassment sat on his face. In the next minute, Tiger turned up in his motorbike gear.

'Traffic. You know you can't predict it,' he said as he took off his helmet and balaclava. 'This is the cheapest and easiest way for me to get to work.' He was expecting sympathy and understanding, but he didn't get any response.

'Well then, I will be back as quickly as I can,' he added, before he rushed to the gents to get changed into his smart suit and tie.

That gear suited him, Luiza thought. *Kind of masculine. Hmm.*

'Come on, Luiza, stop staring.' – said David as Luiza was still watching Tiger disappearing round the corner.

'We have work to do. I suggest you start with reading room one and I'll have a good look at the setting up area first. Then we can meet in the middle. Have fun.' David put his glasses on; he looked more 'efficient' and strode forward looking taller and more confident. He took his notebook out of his bag. 'Right! Let's get on with it,' he said to himself. Luiza did what she was told. She tiptoed to reading room one, to the 'bugs room'.

Colin Foster felt tense and self-conscious. He was hoping he wouldn't get approached. He was unlucky today. Luiza stood beside him as he worked at a bench in gloves and goggles. She asked him to talk to her through the work.

'This is the room where the centralised identification and sensitivity testing is done, which includes the culture reading and reporting of swabs; VITEK 2 identification; the sensitivity testing system, where a smooth suspension of bacteria is placed with open tubes into cassettes for transportation and loading to the VITEK 2 machine; and MALDITOF (Matrix-assisted laser desorption/ionisation time of flight) testing, which provides rapid accurate bacterial identification. It utilises mass spectrometry to analyse the protein composition of the bacterial cell wall, by measuring the exact sizes of peptides and small proteins and comparing against a database. The implementation of MALDITOF has improved the speed and accuracy of bacterial identification. Certain bacteria have their own antibiotic pattern.'

'Do you test control organisms too? Do you record it?'

He looked hesitant. 'I must ask my senior on that one.'

'Are the error logs up to date?'

'Yes,' he said firmly.

'Thanks, Colin.' She tucked her iPad back into its cover. 'I'll come back later.'

Meanwhile, David was in the setting up area. He was seated, and leaning rather too intimately towards a young woman who wore a very short skirt under her lab coat. Her badge said 'Virginia Carlucchio: Biomedical Scientist'.

You don't look like a virgin, girl, he thought briefly, and he tried not to be entranced by her eyelashes. Were they real? He didn't care whether they were or not. Everything about Virginia seemed magnetic. Her confidence, her smile. She was wearing red lipstick and David noticed a silver ankle chain on her right ankle as she was making up an antibiotic disc set when he approached her. He watched, fascinated, and suddenly pulled himself together.

'Tell me, Virginia, how do you organise the work in this section?' he asked politely.

'In this section, specimens are processed like HVS (high vaginal swabs), wounds, MRSA and resistance screening (gentamicin and carbopenemase). Swabs are cultured on different culture plates. Selective and non-selective media. This section is normally run by MLAs.' She was pointing at Andy, who could hardly be seen behind the tower of plates.

'There is more work then we can chew.' He was grinning as he said it with a northern accent.

David acknowledged Andy's remark and turned to Virginia, who carried on with her presentation.

'There is a lot of "streaking and spreading" in this section. I mean plates. Ha ha.' She winked at David. She enjoyed being the centre of attention. She always had good ideas and one day she would be a senior. She knew that. She took a deep breath and said in a professional manner, 'Urines are tested using an automated analyser for sediment examination, called a SEDIMAX machine, an optical system which captures images to gain information about particles in the sample with an on-screen review. It is a fast method where negative results can be reported in a few minutes and it is usually run by an MLA.'

'But sometimes it doesn't work and a BMS has to do manual microscopy.' Carla, a short and chubby MLA with long red hair in plaits reaching her waist, butted into the conversation. She was dressed in proper PPE with a tight laboratory coat, visor, gloves, the lot. She was prepared for the inspection as her supervisor told her to be, but she regretted speaking now, as she realised it hadn't been the right thing to say.

She usually talked fast, but this time her speech got even faster as a result of being nervous. 'But... you know, we call the engineer as quickly as possible... because of the backlog, you know.' She sighed in embarrassment. 'Here is the number, see?' She said in an accent.

She had never experienced an inspection before and she was worried about her job. She always wanted to do her best and please Tiger, who was in charge of the MLAs. Her moon face gave a beaming smile.

'Hmm!' David looked up, with a stiff upper lip; his face was showing some kind of satisfaction as he recorded that information on his notepad in red. He moved slowly towards the next workstation, the stool bench. A big sigh of relief came from Carla.

'Now let me pass you to Alexa, who will explain everything in this section,' said Virginia. 'I have to get on with my work. We are extremely busy with our backlog. Sorry.' She tiptoed away with confidence.

'Ah, okay, thanks, Virginia.

David was disappointed, as he expected Virginia to carry on the introduction.

'Hi, pleased to meet you. My name is Alexa. I'm in charge of this section.' An attractive BMS with long, black, curly hair was greeting him with sparkly eyes. She noticed that David was staring at her name badge.

'Ah, I am called Alexa because I know everything. I have a photographic memory too. Very lucky, I guess. It is a gift. My colleagues come to me if they don't know something, and I am glad to help. Now I will explain how we process stool samples. Please feel free to interrupt me if you have a specific question.'

'Right, thank you, Alexa.' David put his glasses on and got his notepad out ready for action.

'Stools are tested using a BDMAX machine, a molecular diagnostics PCR (polymerase chain reaction). It is used to check for the most common enteric pathogens like salmonella, shigella, campylobacter and verotoxin-producing E. coli, with the use of the enteric panel.' Alexa took a deep breath. She knew all of this by heart.

'We also test for parasites using a concentrated method, which uses Midi Parasep and is checked by microscopy in Reading room two. Clostridium difficile and helicobacter testing is done by a machine called a GDH for checking toxins A and B by enzyme immunoassay (EIA) test and PCR rapid test, to confirm the presence of the toxin.' She had a close look at the inspector; she wasn't sure how much he had taken in. David looked dazed. *Is it too much for him?* she thought, but carried on, as David remained silent.

'Now I will get Virginia to explain how we set up the respiratory samples. Virginia, would you explain the respiratory bench, please?' She called her over.

'Thank you, Alexa,' said David, turning to Virginia. He felt a slight excitement again as she approached him, clicking her heels, but it was not reciprocated by her, as she was not aware of this and, anyway, he was not her type and was too old for her. She liked her man masculine, strong, with muscles.

She started talking about the respiratory bench, looking a bit bored, as it wasn't her favourite subject. She liked working in the research laboratory; she wanted something new. 'Well, the respiratory samples are set up in the containment level three room,' she said in a monotonous voice and pointed at the CL3 laboratory.

'We do gram stains for the presence of pus cells and microorganisms.' She carried on in detail about what type of samples were processed and how they identified respiratory pathogens.

'Great.' David looked at her with mounting admiration. At last he had shown some interest. 'Are you recording the batch numbers?' he asked suddenly. But she had such a seductive accent that he barely grasped the response.

Ohh! I want to bend you over that bench, girl. Ohh! he thought; his lust was working overtime. He couldn't help it. He watched, fascinated, and suddenly pulled himself together. He quickly made an excuse; he had to go out for a few minutes. When he came back he looked serious and asked her more questions.

'Are your competencies up to date?'

'Well, of course. I am a CPD officer and one day I will be a senior.' She straightened up and looked in the inspector's eyes with a serious look. 'Yes, I will. I am not just a pretty face.'

'I see,' said David, while he looked at her short skirt and ankle chain. 'You must be the sharpest pencil in the box.' He smiled. 'Can I see your folder, then? I might learn from it,' he said sarcastically, but she didn't see it like that.

'Yes, of course. Mine is the best,' she said proudly. 'I also make suggestions to the doctors about the weekly case studies; they do listen to me, you know? Management are very pleased with my PDP (personal development plan).'

'Ah, really?'

'Yeah. I'm sure I will get a pay rise next year.' She winked as she said it out loud.

'Not again!' Everyone looked at each other and pulled faces.

'Anyway, here is my folder.'

'Hmm. I shall look at it later. Thank you, Virginia.' David was scribbling on his clipboard. He was only half concentrating. He could feel that Virginia's eyes were following his movements. He was wondering how to meet her out of hours. He gathered his wits and approached the senior, Tiger Jones, who was sitting at the microscope looking at a gram-stained slide.

'According to the notice over there, it's been some time since the temperature of the cold room was checked.'

'Oh… dear. I did it on Friday morning. It was eight degrees then… Sorry.'

'Let's call it an oversight,' said David. 'This time.' He moved on.

'Sally, would you check all the fridges?' Tiger asked her politely. 'It must be Rudolf, the new guy! He is a little menace. We "inherited" him from the merger. We need to watch him because we noticed the other day that he had unplugged the fridge; he wanted to sabotage the inspection. It's a good job we noticed in time.'

'Will do.' She went off.

It was tea time, now. Everyone deserves their break, to loosen up and release the tension for a few minutes. Jim headed to the sink, when he was approached by Luiza.

'I shall come to the reading Room after the break. I understand you are working there, and you could give me information on how this section is managed and what you do.'

'Sure, I will,' he said with a sigh. He was hoping he wouldn't get picked, but he couldn't escape the questioning now.

'Oh, what is that you are using as hand cream?' Luiza was curious and she put her glasses on to see it better.

'It's Dick Lick, from Ann Summers. Don't you know? It is a good moisturiser. Everyone is using it; it's good for complexion. We use it as a hand cream, others as a face cream… or something else…' He was giving her a saucy grin. 'Maybe you should try it one day. It's really good, honest. Now, I'm off to tea.'

'No rest for the wicked,' someone said in the back of the room.

'Well, I must get some for myself,' Luiza said on her way out to tea.

The staff were restricted to a twenty-minute break. Some went downstairs to AMT coffee bar to enjoy their precious coffee and chat about the inspection, which they felt was going very well that day.

Others stayed up in the crowded tea room, which was shared with other departments. Noisy discussions went on about their appraisal scores, personal development plans and specialist portfolios because if they didn't reach their targets, they wouldn't get a pay rise. This system had created competition and it was causing upsets for some people.

'How come you have a score one and me a score three?' Candida started crying. 'Have you done extra projects and validations like me?' She attacked Anvi, who was treated favourably by her senior, Tiger, because she did 'favours' for him.

'And I have got a three for my behaviour! What the hell is that? I am always behaving well. How do they expect us to work so hard and be dedicated if they don't treat us well?! I want an explanation. I shall go to HR right now!' Silly Sally's face turned red with anger as she looked at her nails. *I'm wasted here*, she thought. *I should be a rep somewhere and be admired as a showgirl.*

'Girls, keep your voices down,' said Tiger, as he drank his coffee from his favourite Superman coffee cup, which he got for Christmas. 'The boss is coming. Shhh…'

It is hard to work with so many women, he thought, but of course he liked the attention from them, and he liked to be popular. He was confident; he knew his charm would work with women; they would fight for his attention, but he was only interested in Marylene.

Colin was just about to say something when Hannah appeared. The room went quiet.

'Tea break is over. Go on, back to your benches, the lot of you! It is inspection day. Work to the best of your knowledge, otherwise we will fail. Understand?'

But Candida, like a spoiled child, was hiding under the table. She had to be dragged out by a couple of strong ladies. 'But I am doing my best,' she was still crying.

'Go and pull yourself together,' Hannah demanded. 'You are a biomedical scientist!'

'OK, I will be alright, sorry about this.' Her face was red, her eyes were bulging, her spikey, coloured hair looked messy.

'I just have to take my tranquillisers,' she said apologetically, dried her eyes and blew her nose. She quickly tidied herself up, brushed back her hair and put lipstick on in the ladies' toilet.

Meanwhile, Luiza was struggling to get drinking water from the water cooler, but in vain. It had broken down the day before. She needed a cold drink badly on this hot day, so she turned the tap on and, to her disgust, the water was running yellow. There had been a burst pipe during the night on the top floor.

'I must be cursed,' she murmured to herself, when Silly Sally passed her, pointing out the plastic containers which were brought up urgently for the staff. Nanu had to treat their staff well, otherwise they don't work; their brains would boil.

'Thank you, Sally.' She gulped the life-saving drink. 'That's better,' she sighed and shook her body. She was recharged and was going back to the lab when suddenly, there was a sharp, continuous noise that broke the air.

The fire alarm bell! Everyone had to evacuate the building.

The staff who had just come back from tea were drifting out of the lab, walking downstairs to their assembly point in the fresh air. There was a lot of chatter on their way down, passing the firemen, who were locating the source of fire. They discovered that there was a microwave smoking on the top floor. It was all sorted within a few minutes; the fire alarm stopped and the staff went back to their designated areas to work.

'Back to the grinder,' someone shouted.

'It's a sweatshop,' said Rosemary, who was holding some rosemary in her hand.

'What is that?' David was curious.

'Rosemary. It keeps the negative energy away.'

'I see… hmm. Where do you keep it?'

'In my bra, of course. Plenty of room there,' she said cheekily. 'My name is Rosemary, by the way. Ha ha. I read a lot about plants and stones. You have to protect yourself here.'

'Ohh!' He didn't know what to say.

Linda Perkins was tottering slowly to her bench as if there was something in-between her legs. She had had a bad night and had a back ache.

'What has happened to your legs?' David asked innocently.

'It's nothing. Not that!' She looked cross.

'Oh, sorry. I didn't mean...' He apologised and felt rather embarrassed, and followed her to reading room two.

Marelyne was sitting up straight at her microscope and was looking intently at a parasite slide. She was an expert at identifying them. Tiger was admiring her and went up to her with an excuse to see her. She was slim and tall with blonde, long hair in curly locks, and she was wearing the latest fashion.

'Did you look at the EQA (external quality assessment) slides?'

'Yes, you can look at them yourself; tell me what you think, Tiger,' she said as she glanced at him with her blue eyes, giving him a cold look. She felt uncomfortable in his presence, as he was looking at her closely.

'What I think is... that you have the best legs in the lab, you sexy...' He winked cheekily.

'Yeah? Really?' She knew that already. 'Did you look at them all?' She glanced at his unshaven face. She did not like facial hair, but said nothing. He was getting closer to her. He would not give up; he was always lucky with women and he knew that he would win her over with his charms one way or another.

'You are looking great today. I love the clothes you are wearing, Marelyne,' he said in a soft voice, with a cheesy smile, while he was stroking his masculine chin.

'Do you like my new T-shirt? I bought it yesterday. I've had a few comments on it,' he carried on and opened his lab coat, revealing his Superman T-shirt. 'Do you like it? I'm the best, you know. You can trust me. Right?'

'Yeah, OK.' She was thinking, *Whatever*. She straightened her back and gave him a tired look.

'Can I see you after work? Hmm? We could go to the station together.' He would not give up. He had never been turned down by women.

'Stop that,' she said. 'It is not the time to talk about such a thing,' she said quietly.

'OK, I had better go back to work before the inspectors come. They will be here shortly. Pina colada after work, eh?' He winked as he walked out of the room, letting David in for his inspection.

What a relief! Marelyne thought when she saw the inspector's face at the door.

David approached Charlie. 'Will you tell me, Charlie, about the workflow in this section of the laboratory?'

'Oh, yes. Basically, this room includes the culture reading of urines, respiratory samples and stools, as well as parasite microscopy,'

'Please see some culture plates of different isolates and microscopy of organisms.' - said Charlie.

'Identification of clinically significant isolates of urines and sputum samples, and the appropriate sensitivity testing is carried out in reading room one by MALDITOF and VITEK. In the respiratory section, we identify organisms that cause pneumonia, e.g. strep pneumoniae or haemophilus influenzae. The resistance screening is also done in this room, where the appropriate plates are read and follow up work is done in Reading room one. Faecal plates are also examined here and parasite microscopy is done as well, as Marelyn will explain in detail.

'There are numerous parasites can cause infection' – Marelyne has taken over the conversation. She pointed at some coloured pictures in the Parasitology manual.

'The most common parasites are Giardia lamblia, Trichuris trichuria and a lot more.

'Parasites can be present in small numbers and may be passed intermittently, so multiple samples are tested, especially when a patient has been abroad and whenever OCP is requested by

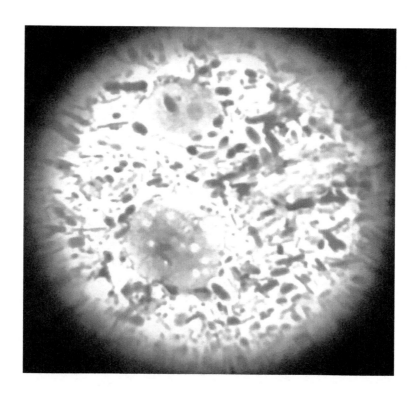

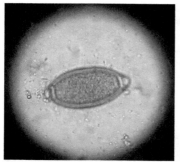

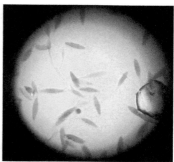

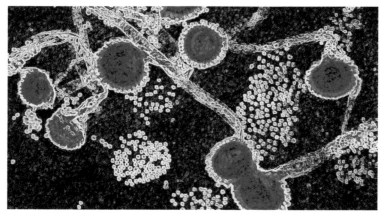

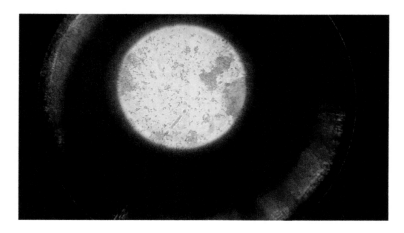

CULTURE AND SENSITIVITY PLATES

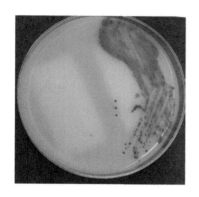

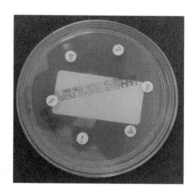

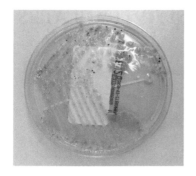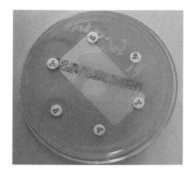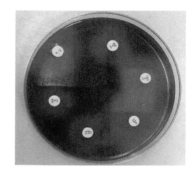

the clinician. 'Thank you Marelyne' – said David and turned to Charlie who was reading the culture plates. On the faeces bench, stool samples are cultured on selective media to identify organisms causing diarrhoea, like shigella, salmonella, and campylobacter or 0157 E. coli, while preventing growth of non-pathogenic bacteria.' - said Charlie.

'Are you culturing for "Yersinia" on a selective culture plate?' David asked.

'No, it's news to me.' David consulted his iPad. 'Just a minute.' Charlie got up, slightly bent because his knees ached, and walked painfully to a file hanging on a hook on the wall. 'What page is it?'

'121.'said Charlie after a pause.

'…Ah, it says yes.'

'What's the date on that?'

He checked the front page. 'The second of April, 2018.'

'That explains it. This version only came out on Friday. Didn't you get a copy?'

'No, Hannah hasn't sent any round.' Charlie returned to his chair. 'The printer's probably broken. It happens all the time.'

'Are your competencies up to date?'

'Yes, Hannah's got my file. May I ask a question?'

'Of course.'

'This is my first job. I feel I'm being made to rush through things that take time and I thought it was just my inexperience. But everybody complains about it.'

'How rushed? Give me an example.'

'Well, I've just been talking to you, which I wouldn't normally be doing. We have to meet our turnaround time and report our findings before twelve o'clock, and if we often fail to meet it, we're marked down. It'll come up in our appraisals. The appraisals are every six months.'

David looked thoughtful.

'We are also expected to take on projects, new targets, to get a "good score",' Charlie continued. 'Our wages get affected by it and it causes an unhealthy atmosphere, because people are competing with each other.'

'Is that unfair?'

'Hmmm.'

'Thank you, Charlie.' David seemed sympathetic. He sat next to Linda Perkins, who was reading the respiratory bench.

She explained that, 'The clinical notes say possible TB. The patient recently returned from Morocco from a riding holiday. If there is any suspicion of TB, the sample gets cultured and processed for TB. All I see is a high concentration of oral flora, but it could be TB, so it requires a special media and a special auramine stain.'

'Right.' Said David, as he walked out of the room and met Luiza.

'How are you getting on, David?'

'I think we should stop here and come back tomorrow to carry on our observations.'

'Fancy some lunch?'

'Sure- there is a nice, large canteen here. Let's go. And after that we could go to the meeting about antibiotic resistance.'

'Yes, of course. We could learn about any updates on ESBL's and carbopenemases.

The seminar room was crowded with enthusiastic doctors and biomedical scientists when the inspectors squeezed in to find their way in the first row of chairs reserved for them. They were the last ones to arrive.

'Hi everyone, and special welcome to our UKAS inspectors, David, Mr Broody, and Luiza, Mrs Cuddle'. Dr Greenwood, a guest speaker who was a tall man with bolding ginger hair in his thirties greeted the audience with a beaming smile, rubbing his hands together, as he took a confident step towards his laptop and projector set up by Joss, his helper. He was knowledgable and he was respected by his staff. He was already appointed to a consultant position in Coventry hospital.

'Our topic today is the antibiotic resistance, the emergence of ESBL's and carbopenemases.

Microbiology has a significant role to play in ensuring that results from relevant specimens are available without delay and ensure that the optimum treatment is delivered within a timely manner.. For example in the management of sepsis. The recognition of sepsis can be difficult as the range of symptoms at presentation can be diverse. However once diagnosed and managed correctly including prescribing an effective antibiotic, the outcome can be significantly improved.

A proportion of patients with polynephritis will have positive blood cultures and some will develop septic shock. E coli is the leading cause of bacteraemia and the urinary tract is the commonest cause of the infection. The progress of septic shock will depend on a number of factors, age, underlying conditions, time of presentation and antibiotic resistance.

The treatment has become more difficult with the emergence of ESB. (Extended Spectrum Beta Lactamase) producing organisms, which often carry resistance determinants to other major groups of antibiotics such as amino glycoside and quinolones.

Antibiotic resistance became more problematical with the spread of carbopenemase producing organisms.

Rapid turnaround of microbiology specimens may be crucial in inhibiting the correct antibiotic at an early stage. Prompt antibiotic sensitivities are also valuable for the patient who is improving because it allows de-escalation to a narrow spectrum antibiotic with less side effects in many instances.

Detection of ESBL production using the double disc method: using cefotaxime, coaxomyclav and ceftazidime. Note the expansion of the zone around the cefotaxime and ceftazidime disc adjacent to co-amoxyclav. The organism is E. coli with TEM-24 enzyme.

See Therapeutic window

See picture 8

The talk ended with loud clapping.

The inspectors gratulated to Dr Greenwood and he acknowledged their appreciation with a smile.

It was a very interesting talk, we never heard of a double disc method. It is a simple but good way of an early detection of ESBL's so therefore treating the patient earlier with a better outcome.

'Thank you for that information. I shall pass it on to other hospitals.' Said David as he turned out to the corridor with Luiza following him.

'I think we can end today's inspection now with a good note.' David said to Luiza. She agreed with a smile.

MULTI RESISTANT BACTERIA, ESBL DETECTION, THERAPEUTIC WINDOW

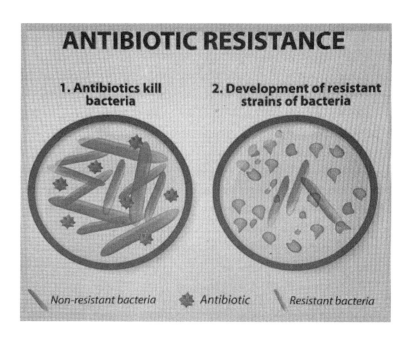

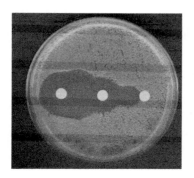
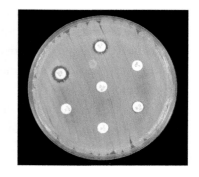

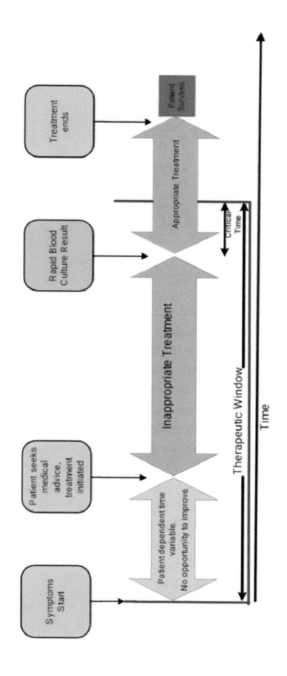

4

WEDNESDAY MORNING

It was a miserable, rainy day. Traffic piled up and people were rushing to work, like Linda Perkins, who had never been late. She carried a large bag on her shoulders, which nearly made her walking imbalanced. It was full; not with papers, but with old clothes she couldn't wear anymore. She wanted to look her best today to impress the inspectors. She was wearing a 'special dress', with a low cut revealing her cleavage. She was feeling sexy today and she couldn't figure out why. She even put make-up on and bright red lipstick. She was about to put the contents of her bag in the bin, her head halfway in, when the inspectors passed her at the entrance of the hospital. David was about to offer her a one-pound coin, not realising that she wasn't taking anything out, but putting stuff into the bin.

Linda looked up in embarrassment and reacted in anger. 'No, thank you! I am a scientist!' She said the last word in a thin voice as she noticed who she was talking to.

It was dead at nine o'clock and the inspectors were waiting for Hannah at her office, but she was nowhere to be seen.

She needed to rush to the toilet with the SOP in her hand. She had to hide some 'evidence', an old method, and replace it with the new SOP she had printed the night before. She had to hurry up. She was anxious, her eyes baggy; she hadn't slept all night.

'Right. It's all done.' She was satisfied with herself. 'Let's hope it will be a good day, God help us!' She took some tranquillisers, brushed her hair and almost ran back to her office, where the inspectors were waiting for her impatiently to discuss the non-compliances they had found so far, before they resumed the day of inspection. It was their last day.

Their agenda for the day was to inspect Reading room three, which included the 'specialist bench' and 'blood culture bench', then Reading room five, the containment level three room.

Passing the doctor's office, David said a friendly hello to the young doctor, whose eyes were glued to the screen of his computer. David's curiosity made him go inside.

'Ahh, you are looking at sexy pictures!' David was shocked.

'This one lights up my fire,' the junior doctor said in embarrassment, pointing at a girl with large boobs. 'We need endorphins, happy hormones, you know, to get through the day. We can discuss it at the case studies.' He winked at him.

'Ah, I see.' David's face was twitching. 'Keep up the good work,' he said on his way out. *I could learn from it, too*, went through his mind.

On his way to the TB room, David noticed that Tom Clark, the Laboratory Manager, was sleeping in his office. His head was touching his desk and he was snoring. He had nodded off because he hadn't slept for weeks. He nearly fell off his chair when Peter shook him by his arm.

'It's the inspectors! Wake up, Tom!'

'What, what?' He opened his eyes, wondering what happened. He shook himself, but he was not worried; he would retire soon. He rearranged his family pictures on his desk and smiled, thinking of his grandkids.

Then he started singing, 'Hickory, dickory, dock. The mouse ran up the clock… la la la.'

David made a note of it in red in his book and shook his head. Meanwhile, there was a strange noise coming through from one of the cupboards in the corridor. It sounded like a dog barking. David stopped, listened and opened the cupboard, when Laura's dog jumped out.

'Curiosity kills the cat!' said Laura, but it was a dog!

'What is this doing here? It's against UKAS laws to keep a dog in the laboratory!' he shouted in disbelief.

'Oh, it's my dog called Honey, she is so sweet.' At that moment, the dog caught David's trousers with her teeth.

'I'm not so sure of that. Get rid of it immediately!'

'But there is no dog crèche in here,' Laura pleaded, but in vain. 'Otherwise, I have to take her home.'

'Do it, then,' David demanded.

'Come on, Honey, my darling, we are going home now. Kiss, kiss,' said Laura.

'*Pfuj!*' David was disgusted. 'Any more surprises? I wonder,' he said quietly to himself, nodding his head in displeasure. He was in shock. He needed to have a break and went down to AMT for a coffee.

Meanwhile, Luiza was approaching the blood culture section and the specialist section with a sign on the door:

YOUR BLOOD CURDLES IN HERE.

She approached Candida Osborne, as she was the section leader of this section. Her spiky hair in rainbow colours had drawn Luiza's attention. Candida started talking very fast and in a loud voice, eyes bulging. She had large, crooked teeth and when she was angry, you knew it.

'The specialist area includes the examination of blood culture,

CSF, any sterile fluids like ascitic fluids or peritoneal dialysis fluids and any tissues. Blood cultures are used whenever clinicians suspect the presence of clinically significant bacteraemia, infective endocarditis, or any infective conditions associated with clinical presentation of pyrexia of unknown origin. The method in use for blood culture detection is the automated BacT Alert machine', which is a continuous blood culture analyser. Culture plates are read, and significant isolates are sent to MALDITOF for identification and sensitivity testing.'

'Thanks, Candida. Can I look at that gram slide?'

'Sure, here it is.' She passed on the freshly stained slide under the microscope.

Luiza was just getting her position at the right height, but the swivel chair was not designed to carry such a heavy weight. She fell on the floor and made a big bumpy noise.

'Ohh! It hurt!' She struggled to get up; she was on her hands and knees when Archie, a strong MLA, ran to her rescue. He pulled her up a bit, not realising how heavy she was, so he dropped her on the floor. He needed help. Half the lab had surrounded her by now and at last she was on her feet again.

'Ah, thank you. All of you,' she sighed.

'What the fuck?!' Rudolf, the new BMS, said it aloud on the HVS (high vaginal swab) section when he opened a specimen pot. 'Oh, pardon my English!' he apologised. 'What is that?' People gathered around him and Luiza put her glasses on to see it better.

'In that specimen pot, what is it?' The sample was small, solitary and unattended. 'What's this?' she pointed. Luiza had already bent towards it. 'It looks like a strawberry. That's the leaf.'

Rudolf looked embarrassed. 'That's what I thought, too.'

Luiza looked harder. 'It *is* a strawberry. Why is it here?'

'I don't know why they sent it to us. It came from theatre, but it is not a tissue. It was inside for two weeks, according to the clinical details,' he added.

'Must have been a great party!' Andreas, a tall and skinny MLA, fell about laughing. 'Where is the cherry? Ha ha!'

'A bit like those things we have to extract from guys in outpatients; you know, cucumbers, carrots, candlesticks...' a doctor commented, who came around to see it. 'The other day, a toilet brush was operated out of a man. He said he fell on it! We couldn't believe it when we saw it on the X-ray. At first, we tried to give it a natural birth by pushing it from the top and asking him to push, but as it didn't come out, we had to open him up. Unbelievable! We prescribed him prostate mycin, which makes you fart but eases the pressure and pain. There was also a woman who had "toy soldiers" put up in her vagina. Seven of them! A whole army! We couldn't believe what people do! Anyway, just a little lecture for you.'

'Oh dear! I must have fresh air,' Luiza gasped. 'I think I am going down to AMT.'

When the desired tea time came at last and the inspectors were out of the way, Laura put the radio on. It was playing 'Lonely'. She was singing in an operatic voice. Music helped her mentally. She was still sad about breaking up with her boyfriend, but in a strange way she felt relieved. He was a player, and he was only using her. There would be someone else; she was pretty enough to find the right person. She was about to go to tea when Tiger came in, asking her to do a 'favour', to read the gram stains for him, which was not expected.

'I am sure you can ask someone else to do you favours, Tiger.'

'Don't moan, just get on with it. It's doable,' he said firmly.

'Why don't you ask your friend, Anvi? The "kindness of a lady", as you said? She will do it for you, I'm sure. You always ask me to do too much. I'm off to tea.'

'You are getting out of control with your whinging and moaning. It's painful to view; "countess of misery", that's what you are.' At this point she started to cry. She had had enough already.

She was stressed, and she felt she was not valued. 'Grow up, stop this. You are emotional. I am your senior and you will do as I say.' Tiger started to lose his cool, but he had to control his temper.

'I will do it in my time. I need a break, like everyone else,' she said quietly, and she took her lab coat off. Tiger was in a shock for a moment, because there was no woman who would answer him back. He watched her figure moving away from him in her tight, green dress.

'Oh, I lost my thread...' He forgot what he wanted to do next.

'Don't tread on it if you find it.' Laura looked back. 'I think you need a break, too, don't you?' She was wiggling her bum; she could feel his eyes on her as she walked down the corridor.

'Anyway, I like that dress you are wearing today. It suits your colouring, matches your eyes.' He winked. He wanted peace; he did not like confrontation in the lab. He decided to join her for tea; he had to be diplomatic and professional.

As he walked out of the room, Virginia came into the MALDITOF room, showing the new BMS applicant round after his interview.

'This is the "bug room", as you can see. Centralised bacterial identification and sensitivity testing is done here. Culture plates come here from all benches. This is an extremely busy bench...' She carried on.

'...and this is the "plonker",' Andreas, the MLA who was doing sensitivity testing, added to the conversation.

'What did he call me?' the applicant whispered on their way out, with shock on his face.

'Oh, no, no.' She laughed. 'We call the antibiotic dispenser that. Anyway, how did you like the place?' she wondered.

'I like your windows... large windows, plenty of light... good place to work in, I think.'

'Hmmm.' It was not what she had expected to hear. 'Right. Now we are going back to the office to fill in the form.'

'OK... what the hell is this! He was looking at the question. It says: ?Sexual orientation, ? Homosexual

What am I?'

'Just fill in the form. It doesn't matter a bit. No worries,' – she said confidently and walked off in her mini skirt, while Dick Foster, service delivery manager, was eying her with the expression of a hungry rodent on his face.

The bleeper she carried went off on her way to the main laboratory; she had to answer a phone call. She passed Jim, who was on his late shift, just starting to put his PPE on, with a visor and gloves.

He was working on a section which he hated so much – the dreaded semen analysis. He did the sperm count and viability testing before culturing the specimen. The form stated the time the sample was taken. According to the instructions, it had to be taken within two hours of reaching the laboratory. The patient had put three minutes on the form. He laughed.

'Jim, there is a phone call for you.' Virginia passed the receiver to him.

A worried voice was heard on the other side of the line. '…I'm sorry I am late with the sample; my train is held at the station.' The patient sounded exhausted, out of breath.

'He must be taking it now, ha ha,' Joss remarked, to which Silly Sally (SS for short) went weak with laughter.

'I must see Paramjit in the CL3 room with this sample before the inspectors come back from tea. It's for TB. Would you hold the bleep for me?' said Joss, heading towards the TB lab and ringing the internal buzzer.

Paramjit, equipped with his green gown, wearing gloves and goggles, had a lot of specimens to process. He had already done the daily checks of the cabinets, i.e., control panel lights on, cabinet safe to use. He made fresh Virusolve solutions, but instead of processing the samples he was busy with revising the SOP word by word.

Talking aloud, he was in a state of anxiety, 'COSHH (the control of substances hazardous to health) refers to an approved classification of a biological agent. The list is renewed periodically. It is relevant to risk assessment for work.

'Definition of "hazard group":

'Hazard group one: organisms unlikely to cause human disease.

'Hazard group two: organisms able to cause human disease and which may be a hazard to laboratory workers, but which are unlikely to be able to spread to the community. Laboratory exposure rarely produces infection, and effective prophylaxis or treatments are usually available.

'Hazard group three: organisms able to cause severe human disease and which present a risk of spread in the community, but for which there are effective prophylaxis or treatments available.

'Hazard group four: organisms causing severe human disease and which are a serious hazard to the laboratory workers. They could present a high risk of spread in the community and there are usually *no* effective prophylaxis or treatments.

'Legislation requires us to have suitable containment facilities for hazard group three pathogens. Staff have detailed training and instruction for using a containment level three laboratory, which consists of a lobby and a laboratory area.

'Negative air pressure is maintained continuously throughout the CL3 suite.

'Procedures carried out in the CL3 laboratory involve the handling of infectious material that may contain hazard group three pathogens. This entails the use of class one safety cabinets in which to handle the material.

'A list of staff authorised to work in the CL3 laboratory is available from the governance and risk manager for the department, and is displayed outside the CL3 lobby.

'The majority of work carried out in the CL3 suite is concerned with mycobacterial investigations.

'A variety of media are used for mycobacterial cultures. PCR method is also used to detect MTB from respiratory specimens.

'Microscopy using fluorescence auramine stain is a valuable means of early detection of presence of mycobacteria in specimens.

'Staff using CL3 are required to undergo yearly competency training and assessment in the use of facilities.'

He tried to be calm; he knew his job backwards, but he didn't like visitors and he didn't know what to expect from the inspection. He became more and more nervous as time passed by; this was the last port of call of the inspectors for today, where they would spend most of their time, as it would be most interesting for them.

When Jim appeared with a specimen bag labelled 'cough for TB', he couldn't believe his eyes.

'What the hell is this? Is it a joke, or what?' He walked to the autoclave tins and discarded it. 'Unbelievable!' they both agreed.

'You will be alright, Paramjit, just do your best.' Jim winked as he walked out into the corridor.

'Ah, I'm sure! I can't wait to get it over and done with!' he sighed.

A few minutes later, the inspectors appeared.

'Luiza, I shall "take care" of this BMS in the TB room. I will bombard him with questions, while maybe you could check the auramine slides? Is that okay with you?' asked David.

'Fine by me, have a good time, David.' She opened the 'dark room', where Tiger was about to read the auramine slides.

She pulled the door so hard that it came off its hinges and she was shut in with him. Tiger began to be worried, seeing her size.

'Don't worry, love, we have all afternoon,' she said in a soft voice, but he sensed that he might be in trouble soon if he didn't hurry up to open the door. He put all his strength together to pull the door open, but in vain. They were stuck. Luiza touched his trousers with her large hands, as if it were an accident.

'Ouch! My balls!'

'Let's get them better, then.' She was stroking them, and had a secret pleasure, looking at him in the dim light.

'That's better.' He gave a sigh. He felt her legs were brushing against his.

'Let's get out,' he said, panicked in case she wanted more. He was worried about his reputation.

He put all his strength together and at last he managed to put the door back on its hinges and they were freed again. What a relief! Tiger was all smiles, now, and the staff started clapping and cheering him. It was the highlight of the day.

'Ahh, what a hard day!' Luiza was exhausted as she wiped the sweat off her forehead. She had to go to the toilet; she had an overactive bladder. 'Ohh, I've had enough for today.' She walked off in embarrassment.

Luiza ran into Hannah towards the end of Wednesday and was mildly surprised. Something had changed. Hannah's posture had improved. She strode forward looking taller, slimmer and more confident.

'Hello, Luiza! I hope you'll have time to come into my office before you go?'

Luiza had half-expected Hannah to go off sick before Thursday. She'd seemed too neurotic to confront anything difficult. So she followed her into her office, thinking, *She's pre-empting an attack.*

The pokey room, to her surprise, was now dominated by a sheaf of gladioli, eucalyptus, nemesia and roses, crammed into a tall, three-litre glass beaker from the Biochemistry labs at the far end of the Pathology floor.

'That's spectacular. Is it your birthday?'

'No. It's Mike from our VP of medical outsourcing for Infection Sciences. My boss. He'll be here for the results. So will the doctor from the CCG. I rang her to confirm.'

Hannah hung up her lab coat, and as she took her seat behind the desk Luiza saw that she – *Hannah!* – was wearing Joseph. That beautifully cut, grey linen dress, with the flattering Nehru collar, was one she herself had admired in the Walton Street shop. *Hmm. How much were they paying this woman?*

Astonished, Luiza took out her iPad and stylus. Hannah began, 'I'd like you to ask me about any problems you've seen since you came. I don't have excuses for any of them, but I do want to put them right if I possibly can.'

'Well, we both know the premises are cramped.'

'We do, although some of the biomedical scientists you've probably met, like Charlie for instance, were working for the NHS in this laboratory long before Nanu Diagnostics took it over, and it wasn't so cramped then.'

'Why's that?'

'We have increasing amounts of private work. But there are plans to relocate that.'

'Really?' *Wow.* Had Hannah taken a truth drug? Was a rival service provider paying her to spill Nanu Diagnostics' beans? Luiza's mind was racing. So was the stylus. 'Oh, I see. May I ask you something?'

'By all means.'

'How does the money work out, then?'

'How do you mean?'

'Well, you have these premises and these staff only because the CCG pays Nanu Diagnostics to look after NHS work.'

'Oh, I am sure it's all above board. I absolutely trust Nanu Diagnostics on that score.'

'And who would have sold your company's services to these private hospitals?'

'Our marketing people… I don't actually know how the money works.'

'I see. Well, that's interesting. So, er… are you compiling data for Nanu Diagnostics daily?'

'I'd like to, but in practice their software doesn't interface properly with three of the systems the GPs use, or in many instances with the hospital's own system. So, if I want to make a global point, like about the throughput targets my scientists are supposed to achieve and how tough they are to meet, I can't access all the data. And Nanu Diagnostics won't license this department to use the appraisal software you recommend because it's too expensive, so I've ended up with everybody writing their competencies out in longhand. Some of them have terrible handwriting.'

'But you can still collect throughput data.'

'Only if I collect and collate it myself and submit reports in PDF by email, which would take weeks.'

'So, the computer interface is sub-standard.'

'Let me get this clear. You have told your bosses two key things. One, that the work rate they want is too high – too high for what? There is no data to show that patient safety is compromised, but morale is bound to suffer. However, as a result of my intervention, the company plans to move the private work. But at the moment we're trying to find a sweet spot where peak efficiency meets peak speed.'

'Sounds good, but to find out where that spot is, you have to go past it. Over the hill and down it into a big hole.'

'That won't happen.'

'Do you feel you have sufficient influence on decisions?'

'Oh yes, absolutely.'

Luiza was absolutely dumbstruck. This woman had been somehow transformed. Well, while Hannah was in the mood, Luiza would probe.

'Tell me, is there a potential conflict when a service provider is providing the NHS with service, but actively looking for outside contracts that pay better?'

Hannah hesitated. 'Certainly, there is. I can see why. If Infection Sciences can't cope, it'll lose accreditation. We have to upgrade equipment and that costs more than the NHS is paying, so we need these contracts, yes. But my bosses absolutely know that Infection Sciences won't be accredited unless it's efficiently run. I feel like I'm stuck in the middle.'

'Thank you, Hannah,' Luiza said, rising from her chair and putting the iPad away. 'You have shed light on the problems we've seen. David and I will be back tomorrow afternoon with the draft report.'

'Good. I've hired the seminar room from one till three.'

'Tell me, have you ever thought of joining the inspection service yourself?'

Hannah beamed. She was about to say so, but that made two close-to-a-job offers in a week. She would take the one that paid better, from now on.

5

WEDNESDAY
EVENING

David disappeared to Clapham at six.

In her hotel room, Luiza set about writing the draft report by the morning. She had been judging the state of the nation's laboratories for years, and knew what to say, the order in which she should say it, and the degree of detail required. She would assess and sum up the lab's convenience of location, ergonomic excellence of layout, staff numbers, management expertise, staff competencies, health and safety awareness, staff morale, everything. The result would be competent, correct and comprehensible.

When she finally sent the document to her iPad and put her laptop on charge, it was half past nine and darkness had fallen. She called her husband, a circuit judge currently working in Lincolnshire. He'd switched off his phone.

She contemplated ordering a glass of wine and a bowl of soup in her room, but decided against it. She needed to break her train of thought.

Twenty minutes later, showered, changed and freshly made-up, she was crossing the hotel lounge towards the restaurant when she glanced into the bar. The barman had curly dark hair, just like… it couldn't be. Could it? It was.

It was Tiger Jones Hartley, from the hospital. She stopped and watched, transfixed. He wasn't a microbiologist any more. He was a barman. He'd surely been a barman all his life. He swiftly lined up two bottles of spirits and two of lime juice on the bar. He sliced a lime quickly on a small chopping board. He twirled a tall cocktail tin like a juggler, filled it with ice from a smaller tin, picked it up, lifted it high, poured both spirits into the tall tin with one hand, did the same with lime juice, added a splash of sugar syrup, opened the smaller tin over the lot, shook vigorously for about ten seconds, accomplished two long pours into glasses without removing the top tin, and dropped slices of lime into them. The whole process had taken less than forty seconds. He placed the drinks on a small round tray and a haughty young woman in a black uniform sashayed away to a table with it.

Luiza's longing for soup was decisively diverted. She wasn't even hungry anymore.

Oh, how I would love to be sipping a fabulous alcoholic beverage made by that sexy young man.

Fascinated, she moved across the room and perched on a tall bar stool. Tiger Jones didn't notice; he was concentrating. Balletically he twirled bottles, tipped out coloured fluids, added mint or fruit or straws as the girl came back with orders. Customers smiled at him as they came in. She saw two men drop ten-pound notes into a beer mug where there was a notice:

Your Wednesday Mixologist: SLICKER Tiger Jones Hartley.

There was a blue rosette with the letters 'WFA' pinned to the card.

She ordered a mojito from the stony-faced girl. Tiger looked up, saw her and did a double take. They smiled at each other. Soon, he came to her end of the bar.

'You've caught me at my proper job,' he said in a soft voice.

'You're exceptionally good at it.'

'I've won a few competitions. World Flair Association. Flair is that all good mixologists must have.' He winked.

'You don't mention your MSc.'

'No, but I don't spin specimens on my elbow at the hospital. Biomedical scientist is my day job. But it doesn't pay as well as this.'

'You make more as a barman? I can't believe it.'

'I am not a barman. I am a qualified mixologist. I have over a hundred-thousand subscribers on YouTube. And it's great to see you here.'

His smile was intimate, his eyes warm, brown and sincere. Luiza almost allowed herself to feel weak-kneed. She was flirting, and he was twenty years younger than she was.

'Any cocktail you want, I can make. I have my own specials. I'd very much like you to try one.'

'Tell me what you can offer.' Her voice came out sounding much huskier than she intended.

'You choose.' He handed her a cocktail menu. The bar was full now. Orders were coming in fast. The menu offered all of the classics and some she'd never heard of.

'Just another mojito, but spiced this time.'

'I'll make one for you. But I'd like you to try something of mine afterwards. Mezcal and grapefruit vodka base, you'll love it.'

'Are you sure?'

'I told you. I make my own specials. And I know what you'd like.' He smiled mysteriously. His charm mesmerised her. She froze for a second.

'And what would I like?'

'I'll tell you later. When there are fewer people here.' He winked. She understood. She could read his eyes. The desire to be touched by him made her feel like electricity ran down her body.

'I shall see you later,' he said in a soft voice.

'OK.' She smiled back at him.

At eleven o'clock, there was a slight knock on her door. She was ready, slightly drunk from the 'special' cocktail Tiger Jones had made. She answered the door, opened it slightly. There he was. He came in and gently kissed her on the neck. Her body responded and gave a sigh. He slowly took her frilly nighty off and she stood there, naked, in front of him, in her suspenders, with fishnet stockings and red high-heeled shoes. It was her turn to unzip his trousers and release his penis from his briefs. Her pupils dilated as she stared at it, amazed by the size, the strength and power.

'You wanted this, didn't you, all day?'

'Yes… yes,' she sighed.

'Hard and deep.'

'Yeahhh.' She started stroking his erect penis and applied Dick Lick gently, which she had bought in Ann Summers the other day. She carried it in her handbag.

'You are drunk on lust and want the big beast inside you, deep and thick, erect, don't you?'

'Yes, yes…'

His mouth connected with the nipples of the large-chested woman. He sucked like his life was depending on it. She loved it and she bit his lip. Then he pushed her onto the bed and put his dick in, slow and deep. He held both of her ankles on either side and watched her face looking at the big, strong cock going in. She loved being pinned to bed, the twist of the tight buttocks, and being held down by his strong arms.

'Finish me off,' she screamed.

'Oh yeah? Look, is it big? Do you like what you see?'

'Yeah! You are a real *tiger*!' she screamed again.

His eyes were bleary; he was like a wild beast by now and his face twisted as he reached another 'level' with the roar of a hungry animal. In the height of ecstasy, her twisted, steaming body was under the control of his beast. Her ankles were clenched by huge hands and pinned down on either side of her head. The force of the love-making thrusts caused the bed to crash against the wall in a loud and aggressive manner. By now, the neighbours should have complained, but not a word.

Next door, through the wall, was unusually silent. David tried to go to sleep but in vain. He was enjoying the erotic, sonic entertainment of loud bangs followed by the screams of Luiza, caught between pleasure and pain.

He suddenly threw the sheets off and pulled down his pyjamas. Influenced and aroused, the sound of a sexual wrestling match next door sent his heart racing and his cock to immediate attention. He jerked fast and hard, and as the noise ceased next door, he managed to go to sleep.

Next door, with her chest pounding, Luiza said, 'You have passed. I shall come back next year to see the standard.' And she shut the door, smiling.

6

THURSDAY MORNING: DAY OF VERDICT

Luiza awoke from a dream about large, furry bees. They were swarming and she was smiling, but they seemed to be getting louder and closer all the time.

Her eyes opened. The hotel room was dim. She was lying on the bed, naked.

Her head hurt and nearby, her phone was buzzing frantically. She leaned over the edge of the bed, groped until she found it in her bag and said thickly, 'Erhh?'

A pause. David sounded surprised. 'Is that Luiza…?'

'Yes, it's me. Sorry, I seem to have… I think I'm getting a cold.'

'Oh. Err…' Luiza looked at her phone. It was twenty past nine. 'Are you alright?' There was a worrying pause.

'Mmm…' She got out of bed and stood up straight, feeling slightly giddy.

Nothing had happened, and she was going to make sure she was never asked about last night, thought about last night, or acknowledged last night. She was not the sort of woman who had hangovers. She was not the sort of woman who made a fool of herself.

'I am feeling a bit thick-headed. I've overslept and have a sore throat. Could we make it ten o'clock, if you don't mind? I'll send you the draft. I just need time to shower and take an aspirin. I'll be down in the foyer. Are they still serving breakfast?'

She ended the call and sat, staring at the curtains. Had she made a fool of herself? She had *never* done that. Not even when her boyfriend at medical school was a rugby player and they were both off their faces from Friday to Monday. What on earth had she had to drink? She was thinking of Tiger Jones. She would have to face him later that morning and act 'professionally'.

Her self-image had taken a hit. She was chastened and dreaded, above all, the feeling that people might laugh at her.

She tried to think calmly. She had realised how stupid she was, giving in to her desire, but nobody knew her here anyway. Her husband would never find out. She would ignore that man, Tiger Jones Hartley, from now on. She took deep, regular breaths. She opened the curtains, drank a glass of water, and tottered into the bathroom. Her clothes were on the floor, and there was vomit in the lavatory. Appalled, she cleared everything up.

As she emerged from the lift into reception, she scanned the faces of the hotel staff suspiciously. No, not a single flicker of derision. Good. *Look forward, not back.* But her self-belief was shaken. Her self-image was dented. She was less sure of her own judgement.

She drank coffee and copious amounts of orange juice, and at 10:15, she and David were sitting in adjacent armchairs in the foyer. She was reading *The Economist*.

David had developed a pink swelling on his lower lip as he finished reading the ten-page document on his laptop. 'Looks like an incisive critic. Tell them to pull their socks up. You're honest about the background issues.'

'I wanted to tell Nanu Diagnostics that it's not helpful to give people more work to do in a shorter time. I hope that the staff themselves come across well.'

'Yes, they do. And as for Hannah, I read the last inspection report and I thought she could have fixed most of those problems ages ago. This tells us the background issues, which surprised me. There's stuff in here that I didn't understand until now.'

'She asked to see me yesterday afternoon. She was different. She wanted us to understand the pressures, but she seemed totally on top of everything. She wasn't at all the flake she was on Monday.'

'Maybe she was just nervous on Monday.'

'We'd better make our way over there… It's been an odd week, hasn't it?'

Following David's gaze, Luiza guessed someone was standing behind her. A Canadian voice said, 'Luiza and David?'

'Yes?'

'I believe you're the inspectors from UKAS? Hello, I'm Mike Timmerman from Nanu Diagnostics – mind if I sit down?' He handed each of them a card.

'Go ahead,' Luiza said. He laid his slender laptop on the table and took a seat, carefully tweaking his trousers up from the knees.

David said, 'Thank you for our accommodation. Great hotel. Wonderful gym in the basement here.'

'Well, we have to look after inspectors, don't we?' Mike flashed his snowy teeth. 'I'm glad to see you here and since you're the star attraction today, I'd like just an idea of how we're doing. I've booked a little meeting room over here so that I can run through your report first, before you present the results to the troops. Let me just find somebody to take us there. Just a minute.' He left and walked over to the concierge.

Luiza said, 'This is a quid pro quo. We get rooms with a view, he gets a preview… he thinks.'

Mike came back. A porter, ostentatiously tipped by Mike, led them up shallow stairs to a private sitting room on the mezzanine. 'There's tea and coffee over there, sir. If you want anything, just dial seven.'

Bowing his head obsequiously, the man slipped out. Mike said, 'So, my secretary's arranged the buffet and presentation over there, but as luck would have it, I need to be on a train out of Euston when it's all happening. I'm sorry about that, but I hope I can pick your brains beforehand.'

'Not really, Mike. The inspectorate is impartial and that includes briefings,' Luiza said. 'Everybody hears our views at the same time, even you.'

'Oh? I'm not trying to influence you. But you see, without accreditation the whole laboratory is dead in the water. What I really want is *informal* reassurance that our contract will be renewed so that we can carry on our programme of improvements.'

Luiza said, annoyed, 'We don't award contracts. We decide on accreditation or withdraw it. In any case *what* programme of improvements? There have been no significant improvements to the layout of the place.'

Mike looked solemn. 'My thoughts exactly. It's a failure of management!'

'With the greatest respect, it's a failure of funding by Nanu Diagnostics.'

'Management on the *ground* is what I meant. People like Hannah Hayward.'

'Problems can't be managed at that level unless there's investment in the location and in conditions of work.'

'That's a socialist point of view.'

'It's a humane point of view.'

'It's political. There won't be any investment until Nanu Diagnostics' future role is guaranteed.'

David said, 'You mean you won't risk spending the money

the labs need until you're sure your contract will be renewed. But unless you spend some money, it may not be.'

'That's more or less the picture. I could do with a cup of coffee, want some?'

He got up and poured coffee for all of them. Luiza said, 'The problems aren't Hannah's. They are yours. You are piling on more work to be done in a shorter time. That's risky.'

'I hope that's not what your report says.'

'I will read out my report at the meeting and not before,' she said sharply. 'I'm so uncomfortable with this. Once again, only CCG committees and boards can decide who gets contracts. But thank you for the coffee.'

'But you know Nanu Diagnostics can't justify investing until accreditation is certain.'

'Come along to the results and you'll know all the answers, Mr Timmerman,' said Luiza, picking up her bag.

Mike didn't like to part on bad terms and Peter had already accused him of being 'heavy-handed' with people, so he said as they all stood up, 'I will be there. There'll be a CCG person there today.'

Luiza said, 'Yes, Dr Price Williams will hear the results. She'll be shown around the lab. But not by us. Goodbye, Mr Timmerman.'

Outside on the pavement, David asked, 'What was he trying to say? Was he going to offer us a bribe?'

'I dread to think. I don't think he knows what he's doing, but I wouldn't be surprised. I must have dropped his card… here it is… Oh. Wrong one.' She went pale. The card in her hand read:

SLICKER Tiger Jones Hartley
Mixologist
075 7501 7501

How had it got into her wallet? She walked in silence with David towards the hospital, feeling terribly insecure. If only she hadn't drunk that second drink.

At 11:45, in the Pathology department, Mike Timmerman's secretary had taken over the seminar room and was bossing a couple of caterers about. They set out a buffet lunch on trestle tables at the back of the room and coffee urns were lined up on another table at the side. The red carpet was down again on this important day. Staff were dressed in national costumes: Jamaican, Indian, Hungarian, Turkish, African, Polish, all waiting in silence for the inspectors' arrival.

A couple of women in black catering company uniforms were lining up bottles of prosecco, glasses and a single champagne bucket, as yet empty.

A wide-screen monitor was set up at the front of the room, and Joss had loaded the programme ready to play and paused it. He looked worried. Once again, the screen read:

Nanu Diagnostics (formerly Multiple Services Solutions PLC)
INNOVATING TOGETHER FOR ALL HUMANKIND

People were coming in. Dr Price Williams took her seat in the front row. Mike Timmerman sat next to Hannah, saying how glad he was to see her there. Ice was tipped noisily into the bucket behind them and a bottle of champagne cradled inside. On the platform, the huge sheaf of flowers, with Mike's note of apology still attached, emitted a steady cloud of pollen, which settled gently on the floor. As Miklos passed it, he began to sneeze uncontrollably.

'God, terribly sorry,' he apologised.

'Do you have hay fever?' Hannah mumbled and lumbered the unwieldy display out of the room, bumping into scientists who were coming in.

All the seniors were in their seats, and the managers, and the doctors. Miklos was still dabbing his eyes and snuffling into tissues.

Luiza and David were escorted in by Hannah. They were most impressed by this suave hang of arrangements, but Luiza felt queasy. They were greeted by the staff clapping. Bright and hopeful eyes were glued on the inspectors with beating hearts.

'Good morning, everybody.' David started his speech.

'This is going to hurt.'- Hannah thought. The atmosphere was tense, the audience tittered nervously.

This is the report Luiza has written and I agree with every word of it. Before I start I'd like to thank Mike, your VP of medical outsourcing for Infection Sciences, for his outstanding generosity in putting us up at the Marriott hotel. Wonderful hospitality and marvellous food. I'll never forget the roast duck with tarragon. A very good wine list, too! Out of this world. We've both appreciated it. You are a great team, a good bunch of people,' he said diplomatically.

'You are all saving lives! Early diagnosis means early treatment and early recovery of the patient, which depends on the knowledge of the BMS to identify bacteria and report the sensitivity testing to the doctors. Working with the team of nurses and doctors, the route of infection can be identified and action can be taken accordingly.

'Resistant isolates can be sent to a reference laboratory for typing, so the origin of bacteria can be traced, matched and identified. Everything you do in the laboratory has to be controlled by UKAS standards to see that the equipment is working properly. Internal and external QCs are done regularly to keep up standards.' He took a deep breath and carried on talking. Everyone listened in silence.

'As we know, antibiotics have transformed human health by saving millions of lives every year. They have revolutionised medicine in many respects, for example the successful treatment of bacterial respiratory tract infections, urinary tract infections, and gastrointestinal tract infections. Without antibiotics, it would no longer be possible to perform organ transplants, cancer chemotherapy, intensive care and other surgical procedures. But our misuse of antibiotics accelerates the emergence and spread of antibiotic-resistant bacteria.

'Today, we see an alarming increase in new bacterial strains resistant to several antibiotics, for example superbugs like MRSA (methicillin-resistant staphylococcus aureus), ESBLs (extended spectrum beta-lactamases), and CRO (carbapenem-resistant organisms). Such bacteria may eventually become resistant to all existing antibiotics. The antibiotic resistance is a growing problem and we will then be entering a post-antibiotic era. Antibiotics are used both in treating human disease and in intensive farming to promote animal growth, where they may be contributing to the rapid development of antibiotic resistance in bacterial populations. Infections can be prevented by antiseptic measures such as sterilising and disinfecting surfaces to reduce the risk of infections.'

We have learnt about the early detection of ESBL's. Dr Greenwood has given us a really interesting talk.

David looked smug. Mike looked smug.

Good start, Hannah thought, with a pleased smile on her face as she polished the champagne bottle in the bucket full of ice. She winked at the staff. The seniors scowled.

'Now, the rundown of our findings. Luiza, are we ready?'

She was consulting – and mostly reading from – her laptop as she proceeded. 'OK. First, the menu. All issues are, to some extent, management-related, and all will be subdivided. We have found seventy non-compliances in all. But do not worry.'

David stretched up and pulled at the neck of his shirt, loosening his tie, as he was feeling rather hot. He started his speech with hypnotic movement.

'One, standard operating procedures; two, internal physical transport and communications; three, storage and disposal of media and samples. Clinical waste bins were seen repeatedly full. Temperature checks were not done on a daily basis. Incubators were not decontaminated. Four, control checks – recording of internal and external quality control checks and reagents. We have found that kits for tests like C. difficile were not validated before use and the spreadsheet was not completed. Five, staff competencies and training records; six, throughput and morale; seven, error logs were not up to date; eight, OPMS data was not recorded daily.'

'You talk a load of brit!' someone shouted.

David acknowledged the comment and carried on with uneasiness.

'Err... hmm. I can reassure you that there are no errors by clinical staff that would cause a major or critical risk to health. There are minor deficiencies, easily rectified. I can only praise all of you dedicated biomedical scientists for doing a meticulous job in sub-optimal surroundings.'

Though mollified, the seniors did not smile.

'However, the *critical* deficiencies, only Nanu Diagnostics' management can resolve. First of all, the standard operating procedure. Nanu Diagnostics provides a rigid template for this, and it's not adequate. The SOP is a flabby piece of work. It does not have an expiry date. It does not contain dates for review and update, and... ownership: readers have to know where the SOP originated. Who wrote it? No guiding mind or writer is indicated. And there is no list of the team's individual competencies. This is a big issue, actually, and it needs to be addressed. Without these details, your operating procedures seem deeply complacent. The person who fills in the form is not at fault; the fault is in the form. The underlying assumption is that everything's fine. Much too vague. Also, workflows: the SOP doesn't outline them by room. It doesn't benchmark competencies or point out where the lacunae exist.'

Hannah scribbled on a pad. A cold wave of fear spread over her face. She felt palpitations. The air was getting tense; you could cut it with a knife now. The champagne was back in the bucket. Colin was worried about his flat. He gave a sigh and he nervously tapped his foot on the ground.

'We failed,' he whispered. His face was elongated as he thought of his mortgage.

'And the blatant problem is, SOPs are on paper. In 2020! Simply because there is no adequate link to the internal computer system. We don't expect to see documents being printed out except in special circumstances, let alone photocopied. Paper takes up massive amounts of space in hospital accommodation here. Surely Nanu Diagnostics must baulk at spending £80 per square foot to store paper.'

'QPULSE is in progress – all documents will be accessible on the internet,' Hannah butted in.

Luiza acknowledged the comment by nodding her head.

'Then to the management of the department. Nanu Diagnostics cannot supply a clear plan of every scientist's expected workflow. Everybody is doing a bit of everything. We think this is a mere money-saving measure. We would like more evidence of an alignment of competencies with tasks.'

Luiza looked up, looked at Hannah, whose tic had become rapid. Charlie wasn't really listening. He wondered why, in midsummer, Miklos had developed such a nasty cold sore. Surely not genital herpes?

Mike was stony-faced. He said, 'Sounds as if we need to upgrade our IT system.' He added, 'Our system's incredibly slow because the hospital one is.' He looked morose. He was thinking, *One more damn thing they'll all need training for. We are losing money on this outfit already.*

The ice was melting around the bottle of champagne that Hannah had bought to celebrate the good news of their accreditation. Different dishes represented everyone's country of origin from all over the world working there. The stuffed olives and the onion bhajis, the brie and the *bierwurst*, the piroshki and the garlicky fava beans, were sweating in their clingfilm and together releasing a rank odour.

Luiza, sitting close to the buffet table, inhaled great gusts of food smells and felt even more nauseous. She got up and slipped out of the room for a few minutes.

Mike's expression darkened as David went on, 'To sum up the issue, Nanu Diagnostics' operating system is inefficient. It fails to exploit individual competencies within the team. And paper-based files are never confidential. The operational manager needs digital data with a digital password system. She cannot unilaterally change company policy. It's for the company's senior managers to engage with these problems. That's our conclusion. Mike, you've only just taken on your job, but the ball is firmly in your court; you'll have to get the hospital to help you. Before we can sign off Nanu Diagnostics' accreditation in good faith, we need evidence of change. So, we'll be back in six weeks. Any questions?'

'Ahr…' he tried to talk, but a sharp squeaky voice came out when Luiza came in. She didn't look well.

'Ah,Luiza, do you have any more to say?

'Ah, yes, yes…' She was hesitant for a moment and took a deep breath. She sneezed uncontrollably. 'Ah, excuse me…'

'Shit!' someone said in the back row. 'This is the last nail in the coffin.'

'Yes. There is room for improvement. You all have your jobs, no worries, but we will be back!' she said with a forced smile, more like a grin. *I have got you guys*, she thought. She was getting out of breath and her feet were tired. She wiped her forehead as she carried on talking.

'It's hot in here. Oh, I better sit down.' She didn't realise that someone had put a whoopee cushion on the seat. As she put her heavy weight on it, it made a big farting noise. 'Oh, what is this?' She took it off in embarrassment. Staff started laughing.

It was David's turn to talk. His face was twitching; he looked like a right fairy.

'He looks as if he is on diazepam… he has lost his sense of humour,' said Tiger, sitting next to the most gorgeous girl, with whom he was hoping to get lucky.

'He is certainly on drugs,' someone said quietly.

'Let's dispense with the formality.' David swallowed so loudly that you could hear it. 'Hmm.' He stood up, firm, head up high, looking stern. He wanted to look official and he demanded respect.

Suddenly, the door opened wide and there was a big draft, blowing his wig off, revealing his bald head cemented round the top.

'He had a brain transplant,' someone whispered. It was an embarrassing moment. His face was twitching. He was trying his best to stay serious and he picked up his wig quickly.

'Storm in a potty,' someone shouted. David felt uncomfortable and started fidgeting. 'There are ants in his pants, ha ha.' They all laughed now.

'I don't like when people think I am stupid.' By this time he was getting annoyed.

'Why? Does it happen a lot?' someone said.

'Right. First of all, I want to thank you for the invite. We had a great time, but there are non-compliances which we have found. They have to be addressed. Otherwise…'

'I will be on the street,' Colin whispered. 'Who will be paying the bills then?'

'Shush… listen,' said Laura.

Silly Sally was just looking at her nails; Rosemary was staring into the air. She was bored.

Mike stood up. 'But don't worry, guys, next time everything will be just fine. Now, let's look at the video; this is the future of Infection Sciences. RoboMedica! I have listened. I am glad you understand that the NHS system is the biggest problem. We at Nanu Diagnostics can improve set-ups like these with advanced technology, and we'll show you the possibilities right now. I know we're all hungry, but I hope you'll enjoy our presentation before lunch. Those of you who read the city pages and follow the stock index will know that we've recently acquired RoboMedica. You're about to watch their five-minute video.'

Duncan murmured 'Stock index? Does he think we're fockin' millionaires? I'm starving.' Trumpets blared. Everyone was startled. Joss had pressed 'go' on the corporate video and the volume was too high.

A huge RoboMedica logo whirled onto the screen to triumphal music.

ROBOMEDICA CORP

As the picture melted into swooping shots around a vast, multi-layered white box, the music became softer, friendlier, more rhythmical. People began to sway in their seats. A confident transatlantic voice announced, 'At RoboMedica, we call this Ma.' Big close-ups against a black background showed samples moving in sweeping unison along a conveyor belt, swinging up a level, piles of plates being lifted by delicate electronic pincers to swirl past in a blur of crimson.

'With your Ma on your team, you're on track to generate crucial medical data seamlessly, smarter and faster. Ma's professional approach helps patients get better sooner. In the AI behind Ma, you'll see the future of liquid specimen interpretation.' A man in a white coat placed a tray of lidless, half-filled flasks into the white machine. 'With hassle-free set-up' – in loving close-up, the machine swung a small tower of slide plates onto another surface – 'that only Ma can manage, it'll prep gram slides' – it streaked the slides perfectly – 'choose appropriate saline, sterile or Müller-Hinton solutions…'

Virginia came in quietly, causing a bit of attention. She loved it.

Why on earth did she dress like that for work?- Colin was thinking. It was disturbing for him to see her swinging her hips along in front of him. That short skirt and those high boots under a lab coat. Whuhh! David's eyes followed her in the room as she sat down.

The rhythmic music continued. The laboratories in the video had no pipettes, not even a sink or a tap. And only one person: one man in a white coat. A needle dropped a tiny amount of solution into a test tube as the voice interpreted the action. 'Inoculate accurately' – the solution wobbled violently – 'agitate thoroughly' – two spidery robotic fingers twisted a lid onto a glass tube – 'cap and de-cap flasks having measured their size and type…' John sat open-mouthed. The machine carried on twirling, fixing and rifling through barcodes and highly coloured vials and plates of liquid as the voice explained, 'Ma reads the barcode on every sample and interrogates the associated care record. Ma can choose the appropriate agar plate method for planting and spreading, and supply the correct susceptibility disk.' There followed a ten-second montage of multi-ethnic life dramas: a baby in an incubator, an old gentleman with a cannula in his hand, an injured woman in A&E, and a woman in a white coat handing medicine over the counter. 'With Ma in your lab, throughput is twenty-four seven. Ma can access the patient's SCR at any time, and accurate diagnosis and treatment is tailored for each case.' A smiling, happy pensioner accepted her medication.

The Ma machine, alone on the screen, whirled to a stop along with the music, as the voice reminded the audience, 'With RoboMedica's Ma on your team, you're innovating for all humankind.'

It stopped. The seniors sat motionless. Marelyne whispered, 'Eyewash.'

Duncan murmured back, 'Our jobs are gone.'

'This is the future,' said Mike. 'Ma may one day be our new partner in delivering care to our patients. But you know, right now, if your lab is performing brilliantly thanks to the team here, it's probably something the CCG would prefer to postpone. Any questions?'

'Yes,' said Tiger Jones. 'How much does it cost?'

'How long is a piece of string?'

'No, I mean the capital cost.'

'That's commercially sensitive information. It doesn't need many people to run it.'

'No, it doesn't,' everybody chorused, 'we don't plan any change in the team at this stage.'

The door opened. Dr Price Williams hurried out the room. 'Excuse me.'

Hannah stood up and announced that everyone should now fall upon the 'multinational food'. The seniors and the doctors got up and began heading for the trestle tables. Mike approached Hannah.

'Where's the CCG woman gone?'

'No idea. She will be back, I'm sure'.- Hannah said.

'She saw the video, didn't she?'

'Of course.'

'Do you think she liked it?'

'She was riveted.'

'If you talk to her before I do, tell her we're going down that road. Efficiency is our trump card from here on in, Hannah.'

People started jostling for space at the table. Wines had arrived to match each national dish, not always to the best effect. Somebody had unfortunately supplied bull's blood to go with the stuffed vine leaves, Tokaji with the goulash and Retsina with baklava. The champagne and prosecco were, as yet, untouched. The catering ladies doled out tiny plates of everything, so people kept coming back for more. John sniffed, piled two onion bhajis onto his plate and took a bottle of beer. 'I'm a creature of habit,' he said.

Charlie, who was knocking back shots of warm sake and chewing something made of seaweed and prawns, said to Louise Baker, 'That's the competition, isn't it? That Ma thing?'

'I suppose it depends which comes cheaper – us or the machine.'

'It must cost more than we do. They didn't say they'd put it in here. Yet.'

'They never do. They say, "we don't plan any change in the team at this stage," and then they sack us.'

'Oh, well. Eat, drink and be merry.'

'The stuffed vine leaves are very good, you should try them.'

Luiza had to dash out of the room; she wasn't feeling very well. 'Excuse me,' she said.. On her return the buzz of argument grew louder. Hannah saw that Luiza was back and sitting alone.

'Are you okay?'

'I am now, yes.'

'Can I get you something?'

'No, thanks.'

'What a shame.'

Joss had brought a wireless speaker into the room, and now he played music that made everyone want to move. Very, very gently he increased the volume. Soon, people were laughing and dancing. David whirled past with Virginia, not noticing Luiza watching from her chair, and both of them disappeared into the corridor. Marelyne and Duncan were giggling – Duncan having smuggled in a flask of whisky – as Mike and Dr Price Williams sat in earnest discussion, before leaving together.

Marelyne headed for Tiger Jones Hartley. Soon the two of them were dancing, too.

'I've never seen everyone so happy before,' Hannah said, with a foolish smile. 'But it's half past two. Are you ready for champagne now, Luiza?'

'Oh, I think I may be.'

'I think I should make a speech.'

'I wouldn't if I were you,' Luiza said. 'As long as they have a job, and bacteria exists, nobody really cares about Nanu Diagnostics. Or RoboMedica. So today, let's just drink to the future of Infection Sciences, shall we?'

'Sure. We all have ups and downs. We failed but we are trying our best, aren't we?'

'If you can't succeed, try and try again.'

'At least we still have our jobs,' said Rosemary. 'For a while, anyway.' She rolled her eyes as she was pulling faces and rattling her jewellery, which made a noise.

Luiza had seen the instant recognition between Marelyne and Tiger Jones and she felt hugely relieved; not guilty. *Nothing* had happened. Nobody will know.

Tiger was wearing his short-sleeved flowery shirt, showing off his muscles, and tight trousers. This time he was shaved. He hadn't given up with Marelyne yet. He knew he had a unique charm; it may take time, but he would get somewhere with it. He was patient. He was whispering to her about the inspectors when Sally walked up to him.

'Tiger, are we going to the chicken shop?' she said in a childish voice as she turned around on her axis, disregarding Marelyne, who was sitting next to him; but Tiger was more intent on chatting up the new BMS.

'Another time, Sally.'

'But you promised! Your flipping imagination, eh? She is untouchable. No point trying; you are wasting your time, honestly. Your charm won't work with her,' she said. She was hurt as there was a 'new challenge' on the scene.

'Leave her, I can cook better curry, Tiger.' Anvi walked up to him. 'Go to Laura instead. She might welcome your approach,' she sniggered.

'Oh, she is an old, broken record,' -said Tiger. 'Not interested.'

'Come on guys, let's have a party.' Hannah's voice was undoubtedly so demanding that all eyes turned in her direction. 'We have champagne, might as well drink it. Cheers!' She lifted her glass. 'We will all have jobs while bacteria are around. But we shall sacrifice some. Chin-chin… to save lives!' she shouted.

'To save lives!' came the reply, in chorus. 'And the queen!' Everybody started singing, 'God save our gracious queen…'

'And let me remind you all to follow CDC (Centers for Disease Control and Prevention)'s suggestion to follow their guidelines on washing your hands properly for twenty seconds. There are some nasty viruses around, like COVID-19.

'Step one: wet your hands and apply enough liquid soap to create a good lather…

'Step two: rub your palms together…

'Step three: rub the back of your hands…

'Step four: interlink your fingers…

'Step five: cup your fingers…

'Step six: clean your thumbs…

'Step seven: rub your palms with your fingers.'

'We will!' everyone said in chorus. Some started singing 'Happy Birthday', others Michael Jackson's 'Thriller', or the Bee Gees' 'Stayin' Alive' and R.E.M.'s 'It's the End of the World As We Know It'.

At that moment, the air conditioner broke down and water started gushing out of the system rapidly. Everyone had to rush out of the room, feeling half-drunk and merry.

'I am going to the gym now, guys; I need my usual workout,' said Tiger, showing off his bare biceps as he put his helmet on.

'Lu, are you joining me?' He gave her a flirty look. She blushed in return; she didn't know what to say at that moment. It was so embarrassing.

'I suggest we all go home now, after this stressful experience,' said Hannah.

'Guys, I look forward to seeing you next year.' A quiet, unsure voice came from the corner, where David was sitting by himself clutching his drink. He didn't feel satisfaction as he had hoped he would. In fact, he felt defeated.

ABOUT THE AUTHOR

My first book Who Will be Your Judge was released and published by Troubador on 28/08/2015 to commemorate the 70th anniversary of VE day and I thought it would be a great idea to incorporate some of the music into my audiobook. It is read by Nathaniel Tapley recorded in SNK Studios London, produced and directed by Edie Watney Judd and edited by Darren Poole. In addition of narration there is music in the background which is giving an atmosphere for the book. The music is written by a talented young composer Laidi Saliasis. The audiobook contains a variety of soundtracks: Britain: War requiem, Charles Parker:We will meet again, Elgar: Land and hope and glory, Ross Parker: There always be an England, Barber: Adagio for strings,Vanessa May: A poet quest for a distant paradise, Elgar: Nimrod from Enigma variations and it includes the Princess Elizabeth's first radio recording.

The mixture of modern and classical music makes it a unique, first of it's kind audio novel which takes the listener back in time creating almost a cinematic effect. The audiobook is available on Amazon, iTunes, Audible and YouTube.

I am currently writing a sequel of Who will be your judge. I have had a film script written by Bryony Davies and I am hoping my book will make to the screen one day. I had radio interviews with Radio Europe by Hannah Murray in 2015 and in Brighton by BBC Radio in 2016.

My second book: Your stools are safe in our hands will be released in October 2020 by Troubador Publishing. It is a satirical comedy about the yearly UKAS inspection. It is educational but humorous, "lifts the lid" on what goes on behind the scenes in the busiest hospitals run by a private company where there is too much emphasis on paperwork and increasing budget cuts. Readers will have to decipher fact from fiction as they discover the often laughable expectations that are placed on the small laboratory teams who are working to full capacity. It also highlights the the importance of the work of the biomedical scientists whose work is very important in the treatment of patients. The book is also aimed to educate people about the emerging antibiotic resistance in the world.